CW00556401

Copyright © Nigel Mitchell, 2019

All rights reserved. No part of this publication may be reproduced or transmitted in any form or by any means, electronic or mechanical, including photocopying, recording, or any information storage or retrieval system, without prior permission in writing from the publishers.

Any person who does any unauthorised act in relation to this publication may be liable to criminal prosecution and civil claims for damages.

Nigel Mitchell has asserted his right under the Copyright, Designs and Patents Act 1988 to be identified as the Author of this work.

This publication was made in collaboration with, and is published by, the Global Cycling Network ("GCN"). The GCN brand is owned by and associated logos are the registered trademarks of Play Sports Network Limited, a company registered in the United Kingdom at 30 Monmouth Street, Bath, BA1 2AP, United Kingdom.

First published in Great Britain in 2019
Reprinted in 2019 (with minor amendments)
Second edition published in 2020

Food photography by Issy Croker
Food styling by Emily Ezekiel
Cover photography by James Cheadle
Cycling and lifestyle photography by Joby Sessions
Cycle racing photography © www.bettiniphoto.net
Illustrations by Pedro Oyarbide, Kevin Peach

The information contained in this book is provided by way of general guidance in relation to the specific subject matters addressed herein, but is not intended as a substitute for specialist dietary advice. It should not be relied on for medical healthcare, pharmaceutical or other professional advice on specific dietary or health needs. The author and publisher are not engaged in rendering medical, health or any other kind of personal or professional services. The reader should consult a competent medical or health professional before adopting any of the suggestions in this book or drawing inferences from it. The author and the publisher specifically disclaim, so far as permissible by law, any responsibility for any liability, loss or risk (personal or otherwise) which is incurred as a consequence, directly or indirectly, of the use and applications of any contents of this book. If you are taking medication of any description, please consult your doctor or healthcare professional before embarking on any fast or diet.

ISBN: 978-1-5272-4924-0

Printed and bound in Great Britain by Hampton Printing Ltd, Bristol

At Play Sports Network we make every effort to ensure the papers used in the manufacture of our books are FSC-certified, are natural, recyclable products from trees grown in well-managed forests.

www.playsportsnetwork.com

GCN
GLOBAL CYCLING NETWORK

PRESENTS

THE PLANT-BASED CYCLIST

—

Your complete guide to plant-powered cycling

WITH

Nigel Mitchell

The nutrition brains behind historic Olympic gold
medals and multiple Grand Tour wins

- FOREWORD -
PURE & SIMPLE

——

Welcome to the first book ever from us here at the Global Cycling Network (GCN): *The Plant-Based Cyclist*. Together with acclaimed WorldTour sports nutritionist, Nigel Mitchell, we've set out to create the complete guide for plant-based cycling. Whether you're just starting out on your cycling journey or are already an accomplished gran fondo or road racer, if you want to ride simply powered by the goodness of plants, this book should help you do it. And not just do it in the general, abstract way, but do it in a no-nonsense, easy to follow and highly practical way. As in, really do it. And keep doing it.

> "A no-nonsense, easy to follow and practical way"

So how did it come to be? Well, it all started following a video we filmed with Nigel back in 2016 in which he focused on the importance of dairy and chicken to post-race recovery; he was – as he says – "quite rightly" pulled up for focusing exclusively on meat and dairy protein in the video's comments. Which got us all thinking. And shortly afterwards, Nigel began experimenting with purely plant-based nutrition and diets to see if it was possible to perform at the elite level on one. As you've probably guessed, he found that it was.

Later on, we filmed more videos with him on the topic (which, incidentally, you can watch here: https://gcn.eu/CanUBeVegan, and here: https://gcn.eu/BeVegan); soon after we all got chatting about the idea of the book and before Nigel knew it, it had become real.

Nigel's many, many years of experience (not to mention a fair few early mornings and late nights) have gone into the creation of this book – all with the hope that you won't need to invest anywhere near as much time yourself, instead taking its shortcuts to reap the benefits of being a plant-based cyclist. After all, the less time faffing with the minutiae of diet plans, macronutrients, or trying to track down obscure ingredients is more time spent doing what we all love: riding bikes – purely and simply. Oh, and having fun of course. Lots of it.

Dan Lloyd & Si Richardson
GCN Presenters

*Dan and Si enjoying those cycling
staples of cake and coffee*

- ABOUT -
WHAT IS GCN?

———

The Global Cycling Network (GCN) is the world's largest and fastest growing community of road cyclists, all bound together by daily entertaining, inspiring and informative videos, presented by ex-pro riders – from World Champions and Grand Tour finishers to Olympic medalists – across YouTube, Facebook, Instagram and beyond.

Need something to inspire you and get your blood pumping, like epic adventures around the world? We've got a lot of that. Want to know what life is like as a pro racer? Yes, we've got that and hundreds of days of live bike racing you can watch every year. And more. Much, much more.

Every day of every week we create unique, informative and entertaining stories from all over the world of cycling to fuel your

> "Fuelling your passion and knowledge for everything bike"

All our videos are presented by ex-pro riders-turned-presenters to offer you a uniquely qualified look into the world of cycling, inspiring through their

passion and knowledge for everything two-wheeled – all with the aim of helping you become a better rider: from tech advice and know-how, riding skills, entertaining features, riding inspiration, racing, and more, you can find it and watch them all for free on GCN.

passion, humour and insight, and placing you at the heart of everything we do.

On top of our daily new video releases, we also have thousands of videos already published for you to discover, browse and watch – including several with Nigel making some of the recipes in this very book – whenever and however you want.

Did we mention that you can also ride with us at our own events and festivals? That we have our own club delivering members exclusive sock designs every month? And our very own GCN app especially for our global community of cycling enthusiasts? Or that you can also find our content in Spanish, Italian and Japanese as well as English? We didn't? Well, we do, and yes you can.

Videos as varied as how to fix your bike, what not to do on your first ever sportive or gravel race, and even how far you can ride a penny farthing in an hour? Yeah, we *even* have that.

So if you like the sound of all that why not saddle up to discover more about us at www.youtube.com/gcn?

 /gcn    /globalcyclingnetwork   /globalcyclingnetwork   @gcntweet   gcnclub.com

CONTENTS

——

CONTENTS

——

RECIPES

WHY A PLANT-BASED CYCLIST BOOK?

—

In short, because plant-based, meat-free or lower meat intake diets have become increasingly popular and, for athletes, coaches and parents, there are very few resources on how to combine reduced or zero meat intake with training and competition.

There is a broad spectrum of people who'd define themselves as having a meat-free diet. From strict vegans, who only consume and use plant-derived foods and products, even avoiding honey; vegetarians, who don't eat meat but consume dairy and eggs, to pescatarians who don't consume meat but do eat fish and seafood. There is also a rapidly growing number of people who, for ethical,

health or environmental reasons, have a part-time vegan or vegetarian diet in an attempt to reduce the amount of meat they consume. They'll also tend to try and source meat that has been sustainably and humanely produced and there are now producers, such as the UK's Laverstock Park Farm, to accommodate this. If they can't guarantee the providence of the meat, they won't eat it. Personal ethics and dietary decisions are obviously very personal and I certainly wouldn't judge someone who described themselves as vegetarian or even vegan but occasionally had a bacon sandwich. That's not my job. My job is to provide the best nutritional advice for whatever type of diet that they want to follow.

Nigel Mitchell

Whatever your reasons, you can thrive on a plant-based diet

I've had an interest in meat-free diets for a number of years with both my mother and wife being vegetarians but my inspiration for writing this book came from you, the cycling fans and enthusiasts.

On a rest day on the 2016 Tour de France I did an interview with the Global Cycling Network (GCN) about the importance of protein for recovery and I largely focused on animal-based protein (which you can watch by typing in the following short-link into your browser: https://gcn.eu/RestDayFood). I rightly received some criticism for not covering plant-based proteins. This was followed by a number of serious cyclists getting in touch with me who wanted to follow a largely plant-based diet but just didn't know how to go about it. There's no doubt some cyclists have been able to

perform at a professional level on a meat-free diet, Nikki and Matt Brammeier (husband and wife, former world-class pro road and cyclo-cross racers) being great examples, but I'm certain – because of a lack of information and support – other riders have compromised the diet that they wanted to eat.

For non-professional riders with less time to train and recover, getting your diet right is arguably even more important than for the pros. I got some great feedback on some meat-free videos (which you can watch here: https://gcn.eu/CanUBeVegan, and here: https://gcn.eu/BeVegan) and a recipe I did for Global Cycling Network (here: https://gcn.eu/VeganPorridge) and it was obvious to me that there was a large, growing and engaged audience for this information.

- WHAT IS A PLANT-BASED DIET? -

It would be incredibly easy to tie ourselves in knots with nomenclature in this book when discussing the different variations of a meat-free or plant-based diet. So, to keep things simple, I'm going to stick to the following five main terms:

- Meat-Free: An umbrella term that refers to any diet that doesn't involve the consumption of meat.
- Vegetarian: Is a diet that doesn't involve meat of any kind (e.g. beef, chicken, fish etc.) but does include dairy and eggs.
- Pescatarian: The same as vegetarian but includes fish and seafood.
- Plant-Based: A diet that doesn't involve eating any meat, animal-based or animal-derived products at all.
- Vegan: A lifestyle and philosophy that completely avoids eating any meat or animal-derived products, and eschews the same across every facet of life: from shoes and clothing, to furnishings and beyond.

*Matt Brammeier raced the
World Tour on a vegan diet*

CAN A PLANT-BASED DIET SUPPORT HIGH PERFORMANCE?

Although, as already mentioned, there are cyclists and other athletes competing at an elite level while eating a meat-free diet, there's little or no hard scientific data to be able to state definitively whether its effect on performance is positive, negative or neutral. A 2017 review paper (Vegan Diets: Practical Advice For Athletes & Exercisers by David Rogerson, which was published in the Journal of the International Society of Sports Nutrition) found very little data but did conclude that a vegan diet could create a number of specific challenges that need to be accounted for when designing a nutritious diet. However, if these challenges are met with good dietary planning and some supplementation, it concluded that: "A nutritive vegan diet can be designed to achieve the dietary needs of most athletes satisfactorily".

One of the main purposes of this book is to outline those challenges and to give practical advice on how to overcome them. There's no doubt that more research is needed but designing and conducting conclusive studies in this area is fraught with difficulties and issues.

"A reduction in meat consumption... does confer health benefits"

For a start, any study on sport's performance faces the problem of finding suitable participants. If there's even the slightest chance that an intervention may have a negative effect, you're not going to find many sportspeople, especially not at the elite level, willing to sign up. There's also still resistance to athletes following a meat-free diet from many coaches. This means that studies are often limited to relatively sedentary populations, making extrapolations to performance sport difficult.

Next, monitoring the dietary intakes of the different experimental groups and ensuring that only the variables you were looking at were different would be extremely complex.

Finally, there's a huge industry in sports nutrition and a massive part of it involves supplements that are derived from animal products, whey protein from the dairy industry being foremost. Currently it's these companies that fund much of the research conducted into nutrition and performance and so, unsurprisingly, meat-free nutrition has received little attention. Hopefully though, with more people and athletes adopting full or part-time meat-free diets and a resulting industry growing around this, the will and the

Lizzie Deignan has been vegetarian since she was 10

funding for research will manifest. Certainly it's heartening to see a number of the big sports nutrition companies now beginning to create products for meat-free athletes. What has been shown though is that a reduction in meat consumption – especially processed meat – does confer a number of health benefits. These include a reduced risk of heart disease, diabetes and certain forms of cancer.

However, it's also important to note that just cutting out meat isn't necessarily a dietary utopia for good health. Like all diets, it's possible and even easy to eat a very unhealthy meat-free diet. Processed vegetarian and vegan foods, just like their meaty counterparts, are often excessively high in sugar, salt, additives and preservatives.

There are also some potential health concerns with the excessive consumption of some meat substitute protein sources such as soya, and I'll go into these concerns more later on in this book. The keys, whether eating meat or not, are to try to minimise processed food, ensure high quality ingredients and to consume a balanced diet that provides all the nutrients your body requires; this is what this book will show you how to do.

I'm passionate about exploring what I call the 'productisation' of food and nutrition, which simply stems from commercialisation and manufacturers wanting to make money. If you can turn food into a product and convince people they need that product, there's a lot of money to be made. If we all ate simple, unprocessed and nutritious food, a number of industries would simply fold and we'd all probably be far healthier. My primary message is we can get almost all we need from our food. I will suggest some nutritional supplements but I would not necessarily only recommend them for people on a meat-free diet but for any athletes whose particular demands may benefit from them.

Nigel is a lifelong cyclist with a passion for effective nutrition

ABOUT NIGEL

—

Acclaimed elite sports nutritionist and clinical dietician

It's no real surprise that I've ended up working in sports, particularly cycling, as I was born into a cycling family. My grandparents were both avid cyclists and actually met on a club run. My interest in food and nutrition was also a result of cycling as, when she was in her 40s, my mother rediscovered competitive cycling, especially time trials, and she decided that riding her bike was a much better thing to do than cook for us. I had to learn to cook or I would have starved!

My first sports nutrition memory was when I was 16 and providing nutritional support for my mother riding the North Midlands 12-hour Time Trial. Her fuel of choice that day was rice pudding; this always makes me laugh as, 30 years later I was using rice with Bradley Wiggins and Chris Froome and rice cakes have now become a go-to fuel for the pro peloton. As a keen schoolboy cyclist myself, racing grass-track and time trials, I came into contact with quite a few local racers including Wayne 'The Train' Randall. He was a bit of a cycling legend in the North of England, renowned for his fortitude and training no matter how foul the weather. He tortured me on many training rides and, to say thank-you, I helped him develop his own fuelling strategies.

I decided that I wanted to become a sports nutritionist but, at that time, there were no dedicated courses or qualifications. The option that was open to me however was to train as a clinical dietician. It's important to make a distinction between a dietician and a nutritionist. To be a dietician, you have to attain a recognised clinical qualification. This qualifies you to use nutrition in a clinical setting as a therapeutic tool and it's a protected title. Anyone can call themselves a nutritionist, regardless of qualifications, so you should always be wary who you take advice from, no matter how impressive their qualifications appear (the UK's Sport & Exercise Nutrition Register provides a list of suitably qualified sport nutritionists: www.senr.org.uk). Throughout my dietetics training in London my focus was always trying to relate what I was learning to sports and athletic performance. I was involved with a number of university sports clubs and teams, providing nutritional advice to anyone who was willing to listen to me.

On graduation, there were few opportunities to work in sport, so I decided to use my clinical training and work within the UK's National Health Service (the NHS). This was an amazing opportunity as I was able to learn how to provide nutritional support for patients suffering from a number of conditions. The transference of this knowledge to elite sport, where athletes are

> *"30 years later rice cakes are a go-to fuel for the pro peloton"*

Grand Tours can over-stress under-fuelled riders

putting their bodies under extreme duress, has been incredibly useful. For example, working with diabetes patients gave me a great insight into carbohydrate metabolism and the impact of fasting. Experience in palliative care showed me how to maintain muscle mass when the body was chronically under fuelled and over stressed; a situation very similar to riding a Grand Tour.

After the woeful performance of the Great Britain team at the 1996 Atlanta Olympic Games, elite sport in the UK was overhauled,

lottery funding introduced and there were suddenly more opportunities to work in, and study, the various fields of Sports Science.

I became a lecturer in sports nutrition at Sheffield Hallam University. This allowed me to teach, conduct research and develop a consultancy. I was able to explore how what I'd learned in the clinical world could be applied to elite level competition. I began working across a whole range of sports including boxing, golf, squash swimming and, of course, cycling.

Nigel's clinical experience has influenced his sporting work

BRITISH CYCLING & TEAM SKY

———

In 2002 I started working with British Cycling (the UK's national governing body of cycling), which was an amazing experience. It was before the incredible successes of Britain's Olympians at the Beijing and London Olympic Games (2008 and 2012 respectively) and I was able to be part of the development of the marginal gains culture that led to all of those medals. The professional side of the sport was ready to change too and, while dubious and illegal methods of recovery and fuelling had been the norm, it was now looking to clean itself up. My experience of using diet and nutrition to support patients in a clinical context could easily be applied to raising the performance of riders competing at the highest and most grueling level.

The more the sport cleaned up, the greater the potential impact of optimal nutrition became. In 2009, Team Sky was set up and I started working with them from the outset. To my knowledge, at that time, it was the only team to employ a dedicated qualified nutritionist. Other teams would obviously pay some attention to nutrition but it was often dealt with by a sports scientist, doctor or coach who wouldn't be specifically trained and would often just propagate outdated nutritional dogma from the bad old days. Compare that to

"I looked to see how nutrition could enhance recovery"

now where every single World Tour team has at least one nutritionist and often a full-time chef too.

It's often said that the winners of Grand Tours aren't the best or strongest bike riders, they're the best 'recoverers'. This is what I really dialed in on when working with Team Sky as I looked to see how best nutrition could be used to enhance recovery. In the past recovery had involved vitamin injections and intravenous (IV) drips to provide the riders with the nutrients they needed. Although these methods weren't illegal at the time, they definitely blurred the line and we wanted to see if we could do without them. I remember talking to a Belgian doctor who was adamant that it was impossible to ride a Grand Tour without injectables. I wanted to know why it was felt necessary to inject rather than ingest the nutrients. The reason that was given was, under the physiological duress of a three week stage race, the digestive system simply wasn't able to cope. I spoke to former pros and they told me that, by the third week of a Grand Tour, they'd be lying on their beds at night with massively bloated stomachs, hardly able to tolerate food, suffering from reflux issues and bad wind. I could therefore understand why a doctor would look at this situation and decide to inject the nutrients directly

Nigel's work helped Bradley Wiggins win Le Tour

into the bloodstream, just to keep the riders going. However I was convinced it was possible to protect the digestive system and that injections weren't necessary. I knew from my work with HIV and cancer patients that, even in those extremes, maintaining gut and digestive integrity was possible and so, those techniques could be applied to Grand Tour riders. We were ahead of the curve on this as, in 2011, the UCI introduced a 'no needles' policy during races but Team Sky had already adopted and adapted to this approach.

When I joined Team Sky, the project was always about winning the Tour de France with a British rider and, in 2012, we achieved that with Bradley Wiggins. It was always going to be hard to top that amazing year as we went straight from the Champs Élysées in France to the Fox House Hotel in Surrey, UK for the incredible London Olympics – which included Wiggins taking the gold medal in the time trial. I knew at the time I was never going to top that but, with the 2014 Tour de France starting in Yorkshire in the north of England – and being a proud Yorkshireman – I couldn't not be involved.

MOVING ON

———

After the 2014 Tour de France I knew it was time to move on and take on another challenge. I'd always aimed to put in place systems and develop a culture within the team that negated the need for every rider to have individual nutritional plans; I wanted them all to be eating optimally. Once I'd achieved that goal, things started to become a little repetitive. I'd annually audit and refine different components of my work so, one year might be hydration, the next in-race fuelling and then recovery. I'd look at the current practice we were using, scrutinise it against the evidence and literature and then bring in colleagues and peers for their input and criticism to try and ensure it was still the best it could be. What I found was that, small tweaks aside, I'd put in place really robust and effective systems right from the word go in 2010. At the end of 2015, after 12 years with British Cycling and six years with Team Sky it was time to move on. I was delighted and very proud of the legacy and good practices I'd left but, for my own development, felt I needed a new challenge. I was involved in the recruitment of my replacements and, indicative of the acceptance of the importance of optimal nutrition to performance, British Cycling employed two full-time nutritionists and Team Sky one; in effect three people had replaced me.

I wanted to stay involved in cycling and went from probably the highest funded team in the professional peloton to one of the lowest. Some people did question this move but it was a good fit for me. I had to work with an English speaking team, which Cannondale, as it was then, was. I needed a team that would be open and receptive to my ideas and, with Jonathan Vaughters at the helm, this was definitely the case. I also relished the challenge of a small budget, having to rationalise everything I did and, working with Jonathan, he'll find the money if you can show him something will make a difference. I started with a two year contract and, once again, it was a case of trying to instill good practice and develop a culture within the team. In 2017 it was amazing to see Rigoberto Uran take second place in the Tour de France for the team, another career highlight and especially pleasing as I'd first worked with Rigo when he was a very young rider at Team Sky. Now the team has new owners – EF Education First – they've got a great philosophy and it's a really exciting project to be a part of.

Even though I am mainly known for working as a nutritionist in cycling, I have had the good fortune to work with many other sports and athletes. These range from Formula 1, swimming and boxing to currently working with the British Olympic Sailing Team, British Athletics and the British Olympic Association as part of Team GB for the Tokyo Olympics. I have a long history of being a technical lead for the English Institute of Sport, along with Honorary positions at several universities. This deep breadth of experience provides me with a unique insight into the food and nutrition requirements of elite athletes. My diary is busy but I still find time to maintain clinical competency by providing a general dietetic service to a local health centre.

Right: Nigel is now at Head of Nutrition at EF Education First

Bottom: In the 2019 season the team racked up 17 race victories

Nigel developed many recipes during his 12-week experiment

TRYING IT FOR MYSELF

—

With this book in mind, I decided to perform an n=1 study on myself and follow a plant-based diet for 12 weeks. I didn't have any particular ethical or environmental reasons for doing this but I wanted to see the effect it had on me, develop and test recipes and experience first hand the challenges involved. I purposely chose a time of year when I wouldn't be on the road too much for work and, having measured my body composition, weighed myself, had some blood work and done a simple fitness test on my turbo, I had one last fried breakfast and began my plant-based nutrition adventure.

I was very strict on myself, even sourcing unfined vegan, naturally hazy beer but I found I really didn't miss meat and animal products too much (unfined vegan beer doesn't contain fish and animal-derived isinglass 'finings' that are used to help separate the yeast from the beer and so help to make it clear in appearance). I think I'd probably slightly overcompensated in the lead up to the 12 week period, overindulging in my favourite meaty treats, so it actually felt really good. Although I wasn't travelling too much, I did have a couple of trips to France and Spain, not the most 'vegan friendly countries', and these were a real challenge. It took a lot of organisation and pre-planning which really made me appreciate the need for recipes for travelling. At home I found the food combinations that gave me the nutrients I required and had fun developing meals and

> "My energy levels were great throughout the 12 weeks"

recipes based on these. Again, as with any diet, eating healthily involved preparation and planning but it wasn't significantly more onerous than when eating animal products.

Over the course of the 12 weeks I lost about 7kg of body fat and gained 1kg of lean mass. If I'm being honest, I had probably put on a bit in the weeks preceding the experiment but I definitely experienced a significant positive change in my body composition. My energy levels were great throughout the 12 weeks and I averaged about 12 hours of exercise a week. From the blood tests, I was particularly interested in my ferritin levels (iron stores) as this can often be an area of concern for those on a meat-free diet and low levels can impact on recovery from hard exercise. However, I saw no drop in ferritin levels during the 12 weeks. The only slight issue flagged by the initial testing was slightly low vitamin D levels. This is very common during the winter months if you live in the Northern Hemisphere as we synthesise most of our vitamin D from sunlight and it's hard to take in enough from your diet. Taking a vitamin D supplement, which I'll discuss more later in the book, remedied this. My performance on the turbo also improved and, although far from a rigorous and thorough scientific study, for me and for writing this book, it was an invaluable experience.

What has also been interesting is that, although having gone back to eating animal

Nigel has dived into researching plant-based diets with a passion

products again, my desire for them has diminished and I'm eating significantly less. Previously I would have thought nothing of tucking into a 500g steak but now I'd really struggle to eat that much meat. I'll definitely be revisiting my meat-free experiment and many of the recipes from it, which you'll find in this book, are now regulars in my day-to-day diet.

From working with and talking to a number of meat-free athletes, research and my own experience, I'm convinced that it is possible to support high level athletic performance with an exclusively plant-based diet. Some dietary supplementation and an organised and methodical approach to nutrition is necessary but it's definitely doable.

Whether you're looking to simply decrease your meat intake, try a plant-based diet period like I did or are already a confirmed vegetarian or vegan, it shouldn't negatively impact your ability to be competitive on the bike. Hopefully this book will reassure and provide you, coaches and parents with the recipes, knowledge and practical framework to eat the diet that's right for optimal health and performance on the bike.

Nigel Mitchell

With organisation and know-how you can eat and ride well

PROTEIN

—

**The building blocks of both life
and on-the-bike performance.**

- CHAPTER 1 -

PROTEIN

———

It's no coincidence that the first chapter of this book is dealing with protein. Probably one of the main areas of concern for any athlete – or parent or coach of an athlete – who currently eats, or is considering changing to, a plant-based or meat-free diet is whether they'll be getting enough protein for optimal performance, health and, in the case of young athletes, growth and development.

When I first started working in sports nutrition protein was not considered that important, the focus was mainly on carbohydrate. However, from my clinical work with patients in palliative care and patients with compromised immune systems, I learnt the importance of protein when the body is under stress.

I was then able to transfer this knowledge and experience to high performing athletes and saw how protein was essential to support homeostasis, recovery from training and adaptation.

Over 10 years ago I was using high protein diets with athletes and found that protein was particularly important when athletes were under the stresses of hard training, multi-day races or trying to lose weight. I was responsible for the first study to demonstrate that high protein diets protected the lean mass of athletes during a period of energy restriction.

"Protein is essential to support homeostasis and recovery"

Although there are definite considerations regarding protein intake and a plant-based and meat-free diet, there's no reason, in my opinion, why it can't be optimal for performance. Once you have a greater understanding of what protein is, its role and where to obtain it, you'll realise that a plant-based and meat-free diet definitely does not have to mean low protein.

→

UNDERSTANDING PROTEIN

—

All proteins are composed of long chains of molecules known as amino acids. These amino acids are often referred to as the 'building blocks of life' and that's no exaggeration. Despite there only being 20 of them, in different configurations, they're assembled to form complex structures in your body and throughout the natural world. Protein typically accounts for 12-15% of our body's mass; when we ingest proteins, our digestive system – using enzymes collectively known as peptides – breaks them down into their constituent amino acids. These are then reassembled and used throughout our body. Our DNA codes for this rebuilding and reassembly process in our cells, the information passed on using mRNA and this dictates what proteins are built up. If any necessary amino acids are missing, the proteins can't be assembled. A good analogy would be a builder receiving plans, ordering the necessary materials but then only being delivered mortar by the builders' merchants and no bricks; he's not going to be able to construct the building.

If our protein demand exceeds our protein intake we are in a state of negative protein balance. In the same way that if our calorie demand exceeds our calorie intake (a negative energy balance) this puts our body into a catabolic state where it is breaking down its tissues. With energy balance this can be great if you're trying to lose some fat before hitting the beach but, in the case of protein balance, you'll be sacrificing valuable lean tissue. During my time working as a clinical dietician, one of my main roles was

Structure Of Protein

Amino acids

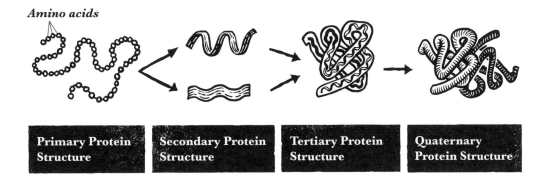

| Primary Protein Structure | Secondary Protein Structure | Tertiary Protein Structure | Quaternary Protein Structure |

UNDERSTANDING PROTEIN

finding ways to use nutritional interventions to prevent severely ill patients slipping into a catabolic state and to preserve their lean mass. Unsurprisingly it is similar during a three week Grand Tour and one of the main reasons, along with hydration, that we closely monitor weight and body composition along with nutritional intake. During a recent Vuelta a España, one of the riders was under-eating and monitoring showed that he'd lost a kilogram of lean tissue. He was underperforming but, by increasing his overall food intake, especially protein, he gained that weight back and his form bounced back for the final week.

Essential Amino Acids

Of the 20 amino acids, there are nine that can't be synthesised in the body from other amino acids and have to be ingested in our diets. These are known as the Essential Amino Acids. Sometimes this figure is increased to 10, as there is some individual variability. Some people lack the necessary enzymes for

certain amino acid conversions and so their list of essential amino acids may be longer. However, the nine amino acids that are most commonly described as essential are:

- Histidine
- Isoleucine
- Leucine
- Lysine
- Methionine
- Phenylalanine
- Threonine
- Tryptophan
- Valine

All animal proteins contain a full spectrum of amino acids and are therefore said to be complete. However, it's important to note that the proportions of amino acids will vary from source to source. For example, eggs are proportionally high in tryptophan whereas pork is far lower. For meat eaters and vegetarians, who consume eggs or dairy, obtaining the requisite amino acids

- PKU -

Phenylketonuria (PKU) is known as an inborn error of metabolism, a genetic disorder, which results in a lack of the enzyme phenylalanine hydroxylase. This means that the individual cannot metabolise phenylalanine, resulting in an excess of the amino acid in the body that can in turn result in certain deformities and abnormalities. The treatment is a diet involving foods low in phenylalanine and special supplements; phenylalanine is metabolised to tyrosine so this is supplemented. Foods high in phenylalanine include soybeans, egg whites, crustaceans, chicken breast, spirulina, watercress, legumes and cottage cheese.

*It's relatively simple to eat a
broad range of protein sources*

isn't really a problem as most of the animal products they consume offer this complete range of amino acids. However, not all animal proteins contain a full complement of amino acids. For example, gelatin, which is derived from animals' hooves and horns and heavily utilised in the supplements industry, contains almost no tryptophan and low amounts of methionine and isoleucine. That said, if you're eating meat or dairy, you'll be getting your full complement.

There is a common misconception that vegetable proteins are not complete but most will provide all of the essential amino acids, however some may be low and the level of the limiting amino acid will reflect the overall quality of the protein. Protein digestibility-corrected amino acid scores (PDCAAS) reflect the digestibility of proteins. Whey protein, which is often regarded as one of the best quality proteins, has a score of 99; soya protein has a score of about 93, and wheat 50. Recent research has shown that the American pistachio nut has a PDCASS score of just over 80 so can be considered complete proteins for adults. Although we have a better understanding of the quality of plant-based proteins I still recommend that people combine more than one vegetable protein source and my mixed beans recipe (on p189) is a good way to do this.

*Our bodies turn over and renew
their proteins incredibly quickly*

WHY CYCLISTS NEED PROTEIN

—

For many years, the nutritional focus for cyclists has been ensuring that they're consuming enough carbohydrates. Attention to protein intake was long thought to be the preserve of strength and power athletes and bodybuilders. However now – with a greater understanding of the role that protein plays and how our bodies respond to training – its importance to all endurance athletes, including cyclists, is now accepted.

We tend to associate protein as being structural, with building and repairing muscle key roles. However, protein is required for many more tasks in the body. For example, albumen, a protein that is made by the liver and dissolved in your blood, keeps fluid from leaking out of blood vessels, nourishes tissues, and transports hormones, vitamins and other substances such as calcium throughout the body. In fact, all of our blood cells, both red and white, are protein structures and the enzymes, which drive all of our chemical pathways, are protein. Because of these multiple roles, proteins in the body are turned over, replaced and renewed amazingly quickly. Typically, in a three month period, all of our proteins will have been renewed. This is one of the reasons I followed my plant-based diet for three months as, by the end of the period, I was literally a new plant-based man! Our diet has to provide the protein and subsequent amino acids for this turnover and, as cyclists, training and racing increases the rate of turnover and, therefore, protein demand.

Referring back to the rebuilding and reassembly process we talked about at the start of the chapter, when a strength athlete lifts weights, ingests and digests protein, gene expression – that process by which information from a gene codes for the synthesis of a protein – is activated to build muscle fibres. With endurance training, the response to training is to code for increased mitochondria production and renewal. Mitochondria are known as the 'powerhouses' of the cells and are responsible for the production of energy. Typically it takes two to three weeks of consistent endurance training to stimulate this mitochondrial production and it's pretty much entirely driven by protein. Although a far more subtle response to training than growing massive biceps, for endurance athletes it's the main reason for their fitness gains. Without adequate protein this simply can't take place.

Mitochondria Structure

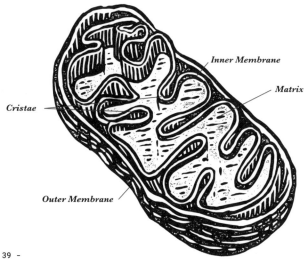

Inner Membrane

Matrix

Cristae

Outer Membrane

HOW MUCH PROTEIN DO CYCLISTS NEED?

——

A male cyclist will typically require 1.2-1.6g/kg/day of protein, with female riders typically requiring about 15% less (0.9-1.2g/kg/day). For an 80kg male cyclist this translates to 96-128g of protein; for an 80kg female rider, it's 82-109g of protein.

To fulfill these requirements doesn't require a huge amount of food, especially for meat eaters. E.g. below is how an 80kg male cyclist who eats meat and dairy might achieve this:

3 EGG OMELETTE	*18g*
PISTACHIOS, HANDFUL	*5g*
TUNA SANDWICH, 1 DRAINED CAN	*27g*
COTTAGE CHEESE, HALF CUP	*18g*
x2 TURKEY BREAST STEAKS	*43g*
500ml OF WHOLE MILK	*16g*
TOTAL	**127g**

The potential problem that might occur for someone following a plant-based diet is the relative bulk of food required to achieve the same amount of protein. For example, if we take the two turkey breasts that are delivering 43g of protein, how much quinoa would you need to get the same amount of protein? Well, 100g of cooked quinoa – a small handful – will give you 4.4g of protein so, you'd need almost 10 handfuls or the best part of a kilo; that's a lot of quinoa!

The issue of bulk in a plant-based diet also impacts on energy availability and balance; how many calories you're consuming versus those that you're using. If you're not meeting your energy requirements, your body may actually be forced to start using the protein you are managing to take in as fuel and, in extreme cases, begin sacrificing your own lean tissue. Unlike obligate carnivores, such as cats, which have a digestive system that has evolved to efficiently use protein as a fuel, ours hasn't. We can, if we're forced to, but it's far from ideal as it won't fuel intense training and racing; it also means that the protein isn't being used for its primary functions of growth, repair recovery and adaptation to training. Obviously, in the extremis case of utilising your own lean mass for fuel, this has serious negative performance and even health implications.

Fortunately, for those following a plant-based diet, there are more protein-dense foods you can turn to and, first and foremost of

Tofu is both protein-rich and incredibly versatile

these, are nuts and seeds. For a plant-based athlete, always having these on hand to snack on is a great idea.

Soya beans – or soybeans – are probably the first that spring to mind along with tofu, which is fermented soybean curd. They're a bean, a legume, and, due to their nutritious qualities, have been responsible in helping stave off famine in the developing world. They're an incredibly versatile product, prevalent in many foods and, when soaked and liquidised, can even be made into a milk. There are, however, two main concerns that people have about soya. The first is the amount of soya that is genetically modified (GM). Although there are no proven health concerns with GM soya, if you are looking to avoid it, there are non-GM products available. The second issue is that of plant or phytoestrogen. Soya is relatively high in phytoestrogen and the concern for male athletes is that it will down-regulate their male hormones and have a negative effect. The research evidence

isn't supportive of these concerns but the answer, as with most things, lies in balance and variety. Eat soya but not necessarily at every meal or every day. When I'm eating a plant-based diet, I love to make tofu burgers and other soya-based recipes but will probably only eat it two or three times each week.

Another option is mycoproteins such as Quorn. These are cultured proteins derived from non-animal sources such as bacteria and fungi. Although this might not sound very appealing, they're versatile products that can be used in a number of ways and recipes. The original Quorn product contains some egg, which acts as a binder, but Quorn has now brought out some egg-free vegan versions.

> "There are more protein-dense foods you can turn to"

PROTEIN SUPPLEMENTS

—

Protein supplements have become a common component in athletes' diets and, while they previously tended to be the preserve of strength and power athletes, cyclists and other endurance athletes are now realising the importance of optimal protein intake. Although protein supplementation is by no means essential, it can be a useful and convenient safety net.

For Vegetarians

Whey protein is ubiquitous in sports protein products and, if you're a vegetarian who consumes dairy, is an obvious and convenient source of quality protein. If you think back to the nursery rhyme, Little Miss Muffet (in which, 'Little Miss Muffet sat on her tuffet, eating her curds and whey…'), Miss Muffet wasn't a bodybuilder but was eating an interim product of cheese making that we call cottage cheese. During cheese production an enzyme, traditionally rennet from calves' stomachs, although artificial ones are more common now, is added to milk. This causes coagulation and separates the milk into the solid curds (the insoluble protein casein) and the liquid whey (containing the dissolved whey protein): Miss Muffet's snack or cottage cheese. The curds are then washed and pressed to form cheese and previously the whey was discarded or fed to livestock. The food and sports supplements industry discovered this source of cheap high quality protein and, by spray drying it, produce the protein powders that many athletes use.

The quality of whey proteins can vary and, when buying a supplement, this is often reflected in the price. This variance in quality is usually dependent on the degree of denaturing that has occurred to the protein during its manufacture. Denaturing refers to a change in the protein's structure, that's often caused by heat, such as during pasturisation or, specifically in the case of whey protein production, during the separation process. Although a denatured protein will contain the same amino acids, it will be less biologically active and not necessarily confer the same benefits as an undenatured protein. In higher quality undenatured whey proteins, instead of using acids and enzymes during separation, a gentler filtration process is used. This filtration is more expensive and, as a result, so is the resulting whey. In theory though, by paying more for an undenatured whey, you're getting a more biologically effective product.

For People On A Plant-Based Diet

Up until fairly recently, if you were following a plant-based diet, the protein supplements available were fairly limited and tended to be based on either soya or pea protein. Although these products did provide a full complement of amino acids, the exact proportions weren't quite the same as their dairy equivalents. This didn't necessarily make them less effective but, if you're training hard and looking to maximise your gains, maybe it could put some doubt in your mind. Fortunately, the sports supplement industry is waking up to the increase in people following a plant-based diet and now, using a combination of plant protein sources, such as pea, hemp and rice, are producing products with the same amino

Supplements can be useful — just don't overdo them

acid profile as whey. With many people also having concerns about genetically modified food, some are also now steering clear of soya or using non-GM soya. These products are easy on the stomach, easy to digest and, unlike many of their predecessors, taste okay too! I even find myself recommending some of these mixed plant-based proteins to meat eating athletes who want to avoid dairy. With professional riders, I find that about 10% prefer to take non-dairy protein products, usually because of negative digestive reactions when under training or racing stress and, for them, these protein products are ideal.

As I've previously stated though, there's no reason why, if you're following a plant-based diet that you can't obtain the protein you need without resorting to supplements. However, if you're new to or transitioning to a plant-based diet and wanting to support an athletic lifestyle, a supplement can be useful until you find a dietary routine that works for you. Also, just like cyclists who eat meat or dairy, sometimes – such as when you've just finished a hard ride and can't eat properly for a while – the ease and convenience of a protein powder is hard to beat.

WHEN TO EAT PROTEIN

—

The crucial fact with protein is that, unlike fats and carbohydrates, we don't have stores within our bodies. All the protein in our body is serving an active or structural function. The constant turnover of proteins previously discussed results in a mixture of amino acids being available in the cell. This mixture is referred to as the amino acid pool but, as it's constantly being drawn on, it requires regular topping up.

This is done by ensuring that protein figures in every meal of the day; little and often is definitely better than one big protein hit. As a general rule of thumb, you should be looking to consume 20g of protein at every meal and then additional top-ups in the form of regular snacks. A key time for protein consumption, along with post-exercise – which we will discuss later in the book – is just before going to bed. It's while we sleep that our bodies repair themselves but, if the materials for that repair aren't supplied, it's easy for it to slip into a catabolic state.

> "Little and often is definitely better than one big protein hit"

Bedtime snack ideas that provide 10-15g of protein at supper time to support recovery and adaptation:

- Soya Yoghurt (250g)
- Pistachio Nuts (100g)
- Plant-based Protein Supplement (one 20g scoop)

Hitting Your Protein Targets

If our 80kg rider (which I referred to earlier) was to switch to a plant-based diet, the example opposite outlines how they could manage their protein intake; it can be challenging, but not impossible, to achieve a high protein intake from regular foods alone on a plant-based diet.

We can see in the table opposite that this diet will provide just over 103g of protein from foods alone. This is from all food consumed and, although it shows that protein can come from some unexpected sources and does certainly add up, it's still below the 127g our meat eater consumed from obvious protein sources alone.

This intake of just over 100g is going to be adequate for most days and requirements. However to achieve a higher intake, which may be of benefit when you are in harder training or trying to increase lean muscle, then including some mixed vegetable protein supplements can be really useful as a top up. The two servings in this example bump his protein intake up to 131g.

FOOD	QUANTITY	PROTEIN
BREAKFAST		
ALMOND MILK	*150g*	*0.6g*
MIXED VEGETABLE PROTEIN	*20g*	*15.7g*
OAT	*60g*	*6.5g*
SEED BERRY AND NUT MIX	*50g*	*8.3g*
SNACK		
PISTACHIO NUTS	*50g*	*5g*
LUNCH		
HUMMUS	*100g*	*7.8g*
MIXED BEAN SALAD	*200g*	*10.2g*
WHOLEMEAL PITA BREAD	*90g*	*8.3g*
SNACK		
BANANAS RAW FLESH ONLY (weight with skin)	*158g*	*1.3g*
SOYA MILK	*100g*	*3.1g*
MIXED NUTS	*50g*	*8.5g*
EVENING MEAL		
QUORN BOLOGNESE	*500g*	*26.7g*
MIXED GRAINS	*250g*	*9.2g*
SUPPER		
MIXED VEGETABLE PROTEIN	*20g*	*15.7g*
SOYA YOGURT	*125g*	*4g*
TOTAL		**131g**

- SUMMARY -
YES YOU CAN!

———

The main take home message from this chapter is that it's perfectly possible to obtain the protein you require to train and race while following a plant-based diet. Achieving this will, though, require some thought, planning and ensuring that you take in your protein from as wide and varied a range of plant-based sources as possible.

Building Blocks Of Life

Amino acids, which are assembled to form proteins, are rightly referred to as the building blocks of life. There are a number of these amino acids, known as 'essential amino acids', which our bodies can't synthesise and so have to be ingested. Animal protein sources will provide all of these essential amino acids but, although there are some 'complete' plant sources, it's by eating a considered and varied plant-based diet that you'll guarantee getting them in.

Not Just For Bodybuilders

A focus on protein intake used to be the preserve of strength and power athletes with cyclists and other endurance athletes tending to prioritise carbohydrates. However, along with playing a huge number of key roles in normal body functioning, we now appreciate the vital role played by protein in supporting physiological adaptation to endurance training.

Supplements

Plant-based protein supplements have improved significantly, in terms of taste, quality and availability, in recent years. Although it is possible to obtain an adequate protein intake without resorting to supplements, they can be very useful. If you're training hard, looking to build lean mass or for a quick and convenient protein hit post-ride, they're hard to beat. Also, if you're transitioning to a plant-based diet and are still getting your head round exactly what to eat or are really training hard, they can provide a handy safety net. In addition to the protein supplements already discussed in this chapter, you may also want to consider including branched-chain amino acid supplements, commonly known as BCAAs, to aid protein synthesis and muscle growth during hard training periods (turn to p120 to read more about branched-chain amino acids).

Amount And Timing

Always refer to the basic requirements you'll need: a male cyclist will typically require 1.2-1.6g/kg/day of protein, with female riders requiring about 15% less (0.9-1.2g/kg/day). There are plenty of easy to use online diet trackers that will allow you to check this. Try to ensure that protein features in every meal, top up with protein-rich snacks and prioritise protein intake post-workout and just before you go to bed.

"Dan, you can ride and race on plants alone — but not beer"

FATS

—

Fats aren't actually bad – not by a long stretch. They're *essential*. No, really.

- CHAPTER 2 -

FATS

Along with protein, another significant concern for the meat-free cyclist, especially if following a strict plant-based diet, can be that they're getting enough – and the right sort of – fats. For a long time, fat was an evil word among cyclists, with a low fat and high carbohydrate diet the norm for the majority of endurance athletes. However, in recent years, we've come to appreciate the vital role that fats play in both performance and health.

In fact, some athletes and nutritionists have gone too far the other way, utilising a high fat and low carbohydrate approach to fuelling at all times. Although such diets can have their place for certain events, training blocks and athlete types, they're not the performance panaceas that many adherents make them out to be; and we'll discuss them specifically later on in this chapter. However, let's first look at what fats are and how we use them.

UNDERSTANDING FATS

—

In the same way that proteins are composed of long chains of amino acids and carbohydrates are chains of simple sugars, fats are assembled from their own building blocks: fatty acids. When we consume fat, enzymes known as lipases break the fats down onto their constituent fatty acids, which can then be reassembled for use throughout the body. Just like there are particularly important Omega-3 fat. From a dietary point of view seafood, in particular oily fish, is the main source of EPA. You may think that people following a plant-based diet would have less favourable fat profiles than meat and fish eaters but results from a large study which looked at people following different diet styles, including vegans, vegetarians, pescatarians and meat eaters,

Structure Of Fat

essential amino acids, there are also essential fatty acids (EFAs) that must be present in our diet as our bodies cannot produce them on their own. The two primary EFAs are known as linoleic acid (Omega-6) and alpha-linolenic acid (Omega-3). From these two EFAs our bodies reassemble them to form every fat we require.

Alpha-linolenic acid is particularly important because this fatty acid is a precursor for other fats, such as eicosapentanoic (EPA) acid, a found that, even though dietary intake of Omega-3 fats were higher in the fish eating groups, the actual blood fat profile was similar throughout the groups. The researchers believed that the most likely reason for this was the consumption of the precursor to EPA, alpha-linolenic acid. Plant-based foods, including flax, chia seeds and nuts, such as pistachio, are great sources of alpha-linolenic acid. We'll talk more about Omega-3 and Omega-6, their relationship to each other and their importance later in the chapter.

Types of Fat

There are three main forms of dietary fat: saturated fats, unsaturated fats and trans fats.

Saturated Fats

Saturated fats are typically found in animal sources, such as meat and dairy, whereas unsaturated fats tend to come from plants. The terms saturated and unsaturated simply refer to the structure of the fatty acids that comprise the fat, in particular the bonds that hold their structure together. Saturated fats are solid at room temperature.

Saturated Fat

```
      H H H H H H H H H H H H H H H O
      | | | | | | | | | | | | | | | ‖
 H – C–C–C–C–C–C–C–C–C–C–C–C–C–C–C–C –OH
      | | | | | | | | | | | | | | |
      H H H H H H H H H H H H H H H
```

Unsaturated Fats

Unsaturated fats have 'double' bonds and tend to be liquid at room temperature. Rich plant-based sources of unsaturated fats include olive oil, avocados and nuts. Saturated fats have no double bonds and are solid at room temperature. Fat structure is important because these double bonds and the sequence they appear in affects how the body uses them and their function.

Unsaturated Fat

C is double bond

(chemical structure diagram of an unsaturated fatty acid with a highlighted C=C double bond)

Trans Fats

Trans fats are found in commercially produced baked goods, snacks and some margarine. These are produced by using hydrogen to change the structure of an unsaturated fat so it is easier to use in food production. This hydrogenation process will generally make a fat that is liquid at room temperature, such as sunflower oil, into a solid. This involves a profound structural change, a twisting of the bonds, and there's an increasing body of evidence that these trans fats are deleterious to health. As much as possible trans fats should be avoided.

Trans Fat

Trans double bond

(chemical structure diagram of a trans fatty acid with a highlighted trans double bond)

There has been a lot of misinformation over the years about what are healthy and what are unhealthy fats. For a long time, saturated fats got a very bad rap but increasingly we're coming to the understanding that, like many things, with fats, it's not a simple black and white, good and bad case. We need both saturated and unsaturated fats in our diets and, in fact, from a health perspective, the aim should be to consume those fats in as close to their natural state as possible. By avoiding artificially manipulated hydrogenated fats and minimising the denaturing that occurs to the fats we use in cooking, which we'll discuss later in the chapter, you shouldn't go far wrong with your fat intake.

*Saturated fats – like coconut butter
– are solid at room temperature*

THE ROLE OF FATS

—

Although we tend to think of fats primarily as a fuel, they also play a key role in many of our body's structures and processes.

The vast majority of cells in our bodies, including muscle cells, are surrounded by their own skin or membrane and that membrane is composed of a phospholipid bilayer. This is made of two opposing layers of phosphate groups, each of which has got a tail – a bit like a tadpole – that is made of fat. This membrane, along with enclosing and protecting the cell, also allows the transport of nutrients into the cell and waste metabolites out. The fats that we eat have a direct bearing on the integrity and function of this membrane.

Fat is used for the manufacture of a huge number of chemicals and substances within our bodies, including most of our hormones. For example, testosterone production is dependent on a much maligned and misunderstood fat: cholesterol. If we're deficient in cholesterol, this can result in reduced testosterone level, already often an issue for endurance athletes, especially those over 40. Fats are important for the absorption of fat-soluble vitamins, including D, K and A, and in the case of vitamin D – which we synthesise utilising sunlight and cholesterol – its production. Also, many of the messenger and transporter chemicals in our bodies have an element of fat within them.

Phospholipid Bilayer

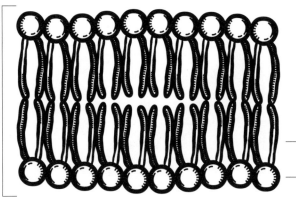

Extracellular

Intracellular

— *Hydrophobic tail*

— *Hydrophilic head*

Fat is our most energy-dense fuel and is burned aerobically

The body likes to store approximately 90,000kcal worth of fat. That's enough for us to survive for about a month without eating. When you look at cases of prisoners going on hunger strike, without forced nutritional intervention, it typically takes them 30-40 days to die. We store our excess energy as fat in adipose tissue as, weight for weight, it's more energy dense than any other nutrient, giving us approximately 9kcal/g. It doesn't matter if excess energy comes from carbohydrates, protein, fat or alcohol, it'll be stored as fat. Interestingly, the number of fat cells – known as adipocytes – you have, no matter how lean or overweight you are, doesn't change: they simply become more of less full of fat.

Fat is also important for the protection of our internal organs such as our liver and kidneys. We can also see this protective role in how fat stores are distributed differently between men and women. Women will typically have more stored fat and it will tend to be around their reproductive organs.

Because of all of these vital functions in the body, our bodies will protect what it considers to be a vital amount. For elite athletes who are striving to get super lean (male <5% and female <15%) this can be an issue as, at these very low levels, the body will hang onto fat and start to sacrifice muscle tissue.

FATS AS FUEL

Each gram of fat typically provides 9kcal, some fats such as medium chain triglycerides found in coconut oil contain 7kcal but this is still approximately twice that of carbohydrates at 3.75kcal. At 15% body fat (slightly less than average) an 80kg cyclist would have an astonishing 108,000kcal of energy stored away as adipose tissue. On paper, that is sufficient energy to fuel more than 10 consecutive mountainous Grand Tour stages without eating anything at all. Unfortunately, when it comes to accessing all that energy stored as fat, it is not quite so simple, since the body has a limited ability to burn fat during exercise.

> "Think of fat as diesel and carbohydrates as high-octane petrol"

When we ride, as we up our intensity, we'll primarily burn carbohydrates. However, at lower riding intensities, when we can supply enough oxygen, we'll also utilise a significant amount of fat. This is not a simple on/off switch but more of a continuum. You can think of fat as being a bit like diesel and carbohydrates as being high-octane petrol. As a rough guide, if you're riding at a pace where you can chat, you'll predominately be burning fat. When you hit the hills or the pace starts to increase, you'll start burning a higher proportion of carbs. If you sprint for a village sign, that maximal effort will be 100% carbohydrate fuelled. During a long ride, we'll use fat stored in our muscles and also release and use fat from our adipose tissue. If at the end of a tough long ride – say, of around four to five hours duration – you were to take a muscle biopsy you'd find the cells to be depleted of both glycogen, our carbohydrate store, and fat.

A lot has been made about the benefits of fasted training as it encourages the body to burn fat, as it's the only fuel available, and makes you more 'fat adapted'. The advantage of this is that it means as you're able to burn fat efficiently and so you'll potentially offset the burning of your limited carbohydrate stores. You won't have to walk such a nutritional knife-edge and won't be so reliant on topping up your carbohydrate reserves as you ride. However, the compromise you'll make during such training sessions is that you will not have enough carbohydrates to do any intensive riding.

FAT MAX

—

In the same way as you have a lactate threshold, you'll also have an intensity point that's referred to as 'Fat Max'. This refers to the intensity at which you can ride where the majority of fuelling comes from fat and, in combination with optimum carbohydrate intake, maintains carbohydrate availability. This makes it crucial for pacing long rides as, if you exceed it for sustained periods, even if you are taking on carbohydrates, you'll run out of steam if you're forced to increase your riding intensity. This is because of a number of factors. The first, as previously mentioned, is that we only have about 90 minutes worth of carbohydrate stores in our body. Second, we can only take in and process a relatively low amount of carbohydrates – this is about 1g/kg, or about 60-80g – however with training and the use of modern energy drinks, which we'll discuss in Chapter 3, this can be increased. Third, we have to ride at below Fat Max for our fat reserves to be able to contribute to fuelling and allow our carbohydrate intake to keep our stores topped up. Ride harder and you'll keep dipping into those carbohydrate stores and your fuelling, without the contribution of stored fat, won't prevent them dwindling to nothing.

A classic scenario that I'm sure many of you will be familiar with is hitting the wall or bonking on the final climb of a long ride despite feeling okay and thinking that you'd fuelled and paced well up to that point. The reality is that you'd probably ridden a fraction too hard and exceeded Fat Max. Up until that point you'd probably felt okay and

been able to push climbs and even contest a few sprints. However, unbeknown to you, your higher intensity fuel reserves – your carbohydrates – were in constant decline. On the final valley road, maybe four or five hours into the ride, you feel okay, maybe a bit fatigued but then, as the road kicks up for the final climb, you start to feel light-headed and there's suddenly nothing in your legs. What has happened is that all of your earlier riding above your Fat Max has finally caught up with you. You probably ran out of carbohydrates in the valley but, as it was flat and you could sit in the wheels, you could ride on 'fat fumes' alone. However, as soon as you needed to up the ante for the climb, the carbohydrates simply weren't there to fuel it and even that gel you took in the valley has just sat in your stomach. It's also important to note that, even when you are riding at an intensity that is mainly being fuelled by fat, your body is still using carbohydrate. Fat itself needs some carbohydrate for it to be metabolised and the often-used phrase that describes this is that 'fat burns in the flame of carbohydrates'.

Fat Max is measurable in a laboratory using gas analysis and the main aim of fat adaptation training is to increase this Fat Max intensity so that you're able to fuel higher workloads from fat. As a general rule of thumb, for most riders, Fat Max is usually found somewhere in about Zone 2, what's commonly referred to as extensive endurance, steady state or where you'd be able to maintain a conversation.

Try carbohydrate restricted training on the last day before a rest day

CARBOHYDRATE RESTRICTED TRAINING

—

The idea of carbohydrate restricted training is to increase fat metabolism. On a technical level, carbohydrate restricted training increases mitochondrial biogenesis, which is the body making more mitochondria. Carbohydrate restricted training is not anything new in cycling but the research is only just catching up with what riders have been doing for years. I remember Sean Yates telling me that when he was building up his endurance that he would have three tablespoons of olive oil for breakfast then go on a long steady ride.

However, although the science is now backing up this approach it is definitely possible to take it too far and there are downsides to be aware of. The problem is, although there are undeniable endurance benefits to increased fat adaptation, training in a carbohydrate-fasted state will always sacrifice quality. Put simply, if you want to go fast, you need carbohydrates. If you try and put any sort of efforts or intensity into a carbohydrate-fasted ride, the quality and the training benefits of those efforts will be compromised. There's also evidence that it can downgrade your immune response and so make you more prone to illness.

When I am advising on carbohydrate restriction, I tend to plan these rides in on the last day of training before a rest day. The reasons for this are because the muscles tend to be a little depleted from the previous day's training, so are 'primed' for carbohydrate restricted work; quality work, which requires carbohydrates, will already have been done and the rider has a rest day to facilitate recovery and adaptation. The rest day is important as carbohydrate restriction creates more stress in the body. Some people also suggest having low carbohydrate the night before but I do not tend to prescribe this with pro riders as, with their high training volumes, their muscles do not tend to be fully glycogen loaded.

> "I recommend some protein for breakfast before heading out"

I do not believe it's necessary to be fully fasted and there's some evidence that this can actually be detrimental. I would recommend some protein for breakfast before heading out. From a plant-based perspective, this could be soya milk/yoghurt, tofu or vegetable protein for breakfast. I also tend to recommend that people eat after about 90 minutes and continue for the rest of the ride at about 40g of carbohydrate per hour. It's important that this type of training should be built up gradually, maybe just starting with 30-45 minutes, the intensity kept low and not overdone. Including one session per week can be useful but remember: although it'll help with your endurance and economy, it's not going to make you any faster and shouldn't be adopted exclusively.

As with most things, the solution is not to adopt an all-or-nothing approach. Yes, becoming more fat adapted is likely to benefit your cycling but that doesn't mean you should make all of your riding carbohydrate fasted. If you look at how a lot of pro riders train, you'll see they'll typically work in three day blocks. On the first day, following a rest day, their muscle carbohydrate stores will be fully stocked and so, the emphasis will be on really high quality efforts. On the second day, there will be some depletion but there will still be quality work, just probably not quite so high an intensity as day one. The third day will be a longer steady state ride but even then it wouldn't be fully fasted. For the start of the ride they'd take on board some protein to keep blood sugar up a bit as some of the protein will be converted to carbohydrate and maintain a less empty feel in the stomach. After about 90 minutes, when the fat adaptation response has been shown to be triggered, they'd start feeding normally on carbohydrates for the rest of the ride.

You can definitely adapt this approach for some of your endurance rides if you want

- KETO DIETS -

Related to fat adaptation are so-called ketogenic or keto diets, which have become very trendy recently. The first commercial low-carb diet was the Atkins diet, which was incredibly popular in the early 2000s. However, like all low-carb and keto diets – whether they're effective for long term weight loss and health, which is debatable – they are definitely not performance diets. If you significantly reduce carbohydrate intake, you make your body think that it's starving and its response is to reduce insulin levels. In this starvation state, the body starts to break down its own tissues to obtain energy and part of this involves the breakdown of fat into ketones. Ketones are an important part of this survival state as the only fuel our brain can normally use are carbohydrates but, as a protective mechanism, it can also use ketones. If you follow a keto diet, you're likely to see elevated ketone levels in the blood after about 36 hours. However, with exercise, you can see an increase in as little as four to five hours. For athletes, the problem with putting yourself into a ketogenic state is that you reduce your body's ability to derive energy from carbohydrates. As we know, higher intensity efforts demand carbohydrates and, if they're not available, performance will suffer. I've seen this first hand with footballers who decided to try a keto diet and, as a result, were hardly able to run around the pitch. In short, if you just want to plod along at one slow pace, a keto or other low carb approaches would allow that but, for any sort of performances, carbohydrates are a must.

- EXOGENOUS KETONES -

Interestingly, there has recently been a lot of research and interest into the use of exogenous (from outside of the body) ketones as a sports supplement. Because ketones can fuel the brain and the working muscles, the use of exogenous ketones effectively turns the body into a 'hybrid' vehicle that's able to burn fats, carbohydrates and ketones. Unlike if you've forced your body into a ketogenic state by cutting out carbohydrates, with all three present, you're able to work at high intensities. The initial research was done at Oxford University and, having created a supplement based on ketone esters that was effective and palatable, a couple of companies have developed commercially available products. It's important not to confuse these products with cheaper ketone salt products, such as raspberry ketones, as these have practically no benefit. Typical dosing is 0.5g/kg taken about 15 minutes before exercise and then at regular intervals throughout. To fuel a typical four hour sportive, you'd be looking at a cost of about $120. The price is in American dollars as, at the time of writing, you can only buy them from the States. Just before the 2019 Tour de France Peter Hespel published a paper* showing that if ketone supplements were taken post exercise during hard training they appeared to improve recovery. This is just one study and it was carried out on non-elite athletes, but even still it caused a lot of interest in cycling. My personal opinion is that, although an interesting area, they don't deliver any real performance advantage over optimal fuelling with carbohydrates and sound recovery strategies, however over the coming years this may change.

to work on your fat adaptation. Start with a high protein/low carb breakfast, such as soya yoghurt or a vegetable protein drink, and then, for the first 90 minutes of the ride, sip on a protein drink. It's vital that you keep the intensity low. Then, for the rest of the ride, switch to regular carbohydrate fuelling and, if you've got some higher intensity efforts to do, do them then. You can also time a café stop

after the carbohydrate-fasted first 90 minutes and use this as a bit of a reset. You won't risk compromising your immune system and you can still get in some quality; important for time-starved amateurs and you'll get some fat adaptation benefits.

Another mistake that people tend to make regarding fat adaptation and carbohydrate

***Reference**: Poffé, C., Ramaekers, M., Van Thienen, R., & Hespel, P. (2019). Ketone Ester Supplementation Blunts Overreaching Symptoms During Endurance Training Overload. The Journal Of Physiology, 597(12), 3009-3027.

You can use a mid-ride café stop to replenish and reset

"The solution is not to adopt an all-or-nothing approach"

fasted training is that it's for the purpose of weight or fat loss. Although you will be primarily burning fat, because the riding intensity has to be low, the total number of calories burned, even over a relatively long ride, will be low. As we've already noted when talking about storing excess calories: it doesn't matter if those calories come from carbohydrates, fats or proteins, they'll be laid down as fat and the same applies to calorie consumption. If your net calories-in

versus calories-out has a deficit, regardless of whether you were burning carbohydrates or fat, you'll lose fat. Therefore, for weight and fat loss purposes, sticking to lower fat burning intensities isn't going to get the job done unless you've got endless hours to ride. You're better off fuelling well with carbohydrates and ramping up the intensity.

However you ride and fuel, if you have a calorie deficit you'll lose fat

PLANT-BASED FATS

———

Hopefully, from what you've learned about the importance of fats in the chapter so far, you'll have come to appreciate that fats aren't to be feared if you're an endurance athlete. If you're a vegetarian cyclist, who eats eggs and dairy, you can definitely keep opting for 'full fat' options without too much concern over the amount of saturated fats you're consuming. For vegan cyclists, it's highly unlikely that there will be any issues with consuming too much fat and it's more likely that ensuring you're taking in enough will be more pertinent.

MEAT-FREE FATS

	SOURCE	CHARACTERISTICS	USES	NOTE
OLIVE OIL	*Olives*	*This is a light greenish oil which contains a good range of fats including both essential fats*	*Great for dressings, light frying, can be used for pastry*	*There are a lot of places now where you can buy the first cold press olive oil which is by far the best to use*
COCONUT OIL	*Coconuts*	*This is a solid at room temperature, provides mild coconut flavour and aroma*	*Great to add to foods such as porridge and rice to increase fat and energy content. Can be used to gently fry food. Makes excellent pastry*	*Even though it is high in saturated fat it is considered to be one of the healthy fats but is not a great provider of essential fats*
FLAX SEED OIL (Also known as Linseed)	*Flax*	*This is a strong tasting oil*	*This should not be cooked with because the fats are easily damaged. You can use it to make salad dressings and some people apply it to dry skin*	*This is really high in omega fats and essential fats*
SUNFLOWER OIL	*Sunflower seeds*	*This is a heavier yellow oil and can withstand higher temperatures*	*Mainly cooking*	*This oil is high in unsaturated fats but does tend to be higher in Omega-6*
AVOCADO OIL	*Avocado pears*	*This is a heavier green oil*	*This oil is used predominately in cosmetics but is increasingly popular for oral consumption. Ideal for using in dressings*	*This oil is high in unsaturated fats and provides a wide range of fats*

Fortunately, there are a huge variety of plant-based fat sources, primarily oils, which tend to be unsaturated fats – although some, such as coconut oil, are higher in saturated fat. On the bottom left is a table that lists common plant-based oils, their properties and how best to utilise them in your kitchen and your diet.

One of the main issues to be aware with regarding oils is, like proteins, that their structure, properties and benefits can be significantly altered by how they are handled and treated. Such denaturing should be avoided whenever possible. Generally smoking or a significant change in viscosity are indicators of denaturing. Many oils are prone to oxidisation by sunlight and are therefore sold in coloured glass or plastic bottles. Oils are also very temperature sensitive and should ideally always be stored at a stable room temperature or slightly cooler. Whenever I travel to Italy, I'll always pick up some really high quality olive oil. When I get home, it'll go straight into my cellar and I'll treat it like a really fine wine!

Outside of specialist retailers, it's very hard to buy olive oil of this quality outside of Italy, Spain and Greece and, even there, unless you know the right people, you won't get the best of the best. If, however, you are lucky enough to be able to source some of this wonderfully green, tasty and antioxidant-packed oil, treat and store it well, only use it cold and savour every drop!

- ONLY THE BEST -

Many of the Italian professional cycling teams will have their own dedicated olive oil manufacturer. Team INEOS (formerly Team Sky) followed this example and one of its ex-riders-turned-team-coach, Dario Cioni, has his own certified organic olive oil farm and supplies the team with the highest quality olive oil. This oil will be the very first pressed and will be extracted using traditional stone presses; using stone minimises the heat the oil is exposed to and maintains a very high level of antioxidants in the oil, making it very appealing to hard training cyclists.

OMEGA-3, OMEGA-6 & INFLAMMATION

—

From a sports and training perspective, a really important issue – when we're considering the fats we consume – is the effect it has on inflammation in the body. You'll often hear people talking about some oils, especially fish oils, as being anti-inflammatory but this is a bit of a misunderstanding. In truth the types of fats we consume are either more inflammatory or less inflammatory rather than actually being anti-inflammatory. So if you consume more of the fats that are less inflammatory, there will be a lower degree of amplification of inflammation. Typically, Omega-3 fats will be less inflammatory and Omega-6 and saturated fats more inflammatory.

> "Fats are either more inflammatory or less inflammatory"

Due to the high proportion of processed vegetable oils in modern diets, which are very rich in Omega-6, the levels in our bodies tend to be disproportionally high. It has been suggested that an ideal ratio would be 1:1 whereas, for many people, it is 1:20. If you're trying to reduce your Omega-6 intake, cooking with olive or coconut oil rather than sunflower oil will help massively. You should also look to increase your Omega-3 intake to further improve the ratio and confer a number of benefits that are especially relevant to athletes.

In sport we use a lot of Omega-3 supplements. I brought fish oils into sport from my clinical work in hospitals. Cancer patients suffer from a stress related muscle wastage known as cachexia, which has no relation to calorie deficit. Even if they're eating enough, it still happens. Fish oils, or more specifically the Omega-3 fatty acid eicosapentenoic acid (EPA), help to prevent it from happening and aids the retention of lean tissue. Hard training or racing is a similar stress on the body and Omega-3 can perform the same function. Omega-3 fats are not only linked to lower levels of inflammation and preservation of lean tissue but also positively influencing blood vessels and protein synthesis.

For plant-based cyclists, obviously fish oils aren't an option but it's still possible to get enough Omega-3 and EPA into your diet. Remember that all nutrients originally come from the sun and are simply passed up the food chain. Oily fish obtain their Omega-3 from eating krill, which, in turn, get it from algae. There are now commercially available algae-based Omega-3 supplements but there are plenty of other plant-based sources.

Two of the best plant-based sources are flax and chia seeds, both of which are also available as oils. You can also easily include the actual seeds in your diet but they should be milled, otherwise they tend to pass straight through undigested. Once milled though, they should be consumed within five to seven days, as the oils they contain are very sensitive to oxidation.

- CANNABIDIOL CBD -

Cannabidiol is gaining in popularity and I now have many riders coming to me and asking about using it. It is one of 104 chemicals known as cannabinoids that are found in the cannabis plant. The CBD is extracted and then mixed with a 'carrier' oil – usually olive, hemp or coconut oil – to facilitate delivery. The CBD oil has no psychoactive properties unlike tetrahydrocannabinol (THC). However there are growing health and wellbeing claims being associated with CBD oil. These range from reducing aches and pains to improving mental health wellbeing. CBD oil is legal and is not banned by WADA (World Anti Doping Agency). However, the extracted CBD oil may contain tiny traces of THC, which is banned, and therefore athletes who may be tested should avoid it even though there would be little chance of the athlete failing a test.

Currently there is a real lack of research of the use of CBD oil in the athletic population and the actual effective dose is not really known; the current advice is to start with a small dose, which can then be built up. I tried a product providing 6.4mg of CBD oil in 160mg of olive oil for a month and found improvements in general aches and pain and overall wellbeing within 24 hours. I also have chronic neck pain following a mountain bike crash in early 1990s but, when I took the CBD oil, this pain went. I then tried a higher dose but observed no additional benefits. I stopped the CBD oil for a couple of weeks and, after a couple of days, my old aches and pains returned. When I re-started the oil, the pains eased again. The findings of my own n=1 study are certainly intriguing but I'm not 100% convinced yet and would be interested in seeing more rigorous research conducted.

- SUMMARY -
FATS

—

Variety

As with protein, the best way for meat-free cyclists to ensure they're getting enough of the right sorts of fat is to opt for a wide variety of sources. Vegetarians who eat eggs and dairy should already be getting a good dose of fat but there are loads of excellent plant sources. Cook and drizzle different oils, mill seeds to add to your porridge and salads and experiment with recipes such as nut butters. Remember, that ratio of Omega-3 to Omega-6 is key and it's only with variety that you'll achieve a healthy one.

Don't Fear Fats

Apart from for certain clinical issues, low fat diets should be consigned to the history books and this definitely applies to the diets of cyclists and other sportspeople. Fats play a massively significant role in our bodies and, without them, good health – let alone high performance – is impossible. Right from the membranes of our cells, the hormones carrying vital information around our bodies and providing protection for our organs, it's no understatement to say that fats are essential for life.

Good Fats & Bad Fats

For many years the simplistic approach that unsaturated fats were good and saturated fats were bad was accepted wisdom. However, now we know that we require a range of fats in our diet and their relationship to health is far more complex. What is certain is that there are potential health implications to modifying the structure of fats during food processing. Trans fats, generally oils that have been treated with process such as hydrogenation to solidify them, should be avoided.

Fat For Fuel

Fat is an incredible fuel reserve that, even the leanest among us, have in abundance. However, it's very much a diesel fuel and, although being able to use it effectively is a key aspect of endurance fitness, trying to rely on it completely is not recommended. Some fat adaptation training can be a good idea but, whenever the road kicks up or you need to increase your speed, you're going to need some carbs.

Treat With Care

In order to get the most out of them, it's essential that you look after your fats. Choose the right type of oil for the cooking technique you're using and, if possible, avoid raising their temperature above smoking point. Ideally store oils in a cool and dark place and, if you're lucky enough to get hold of some really good olive oil, treat it like an expensive wine. Freshly milled seeds are a brilliant source of healthy fats but need to be stored in airtight containers and eaten within a week.

*Coffee and cake aren't bad –
just avoid trans fats if you can*

02

FATS

—

RECIPES

Recipes

——

**Some easy and tasty ways to fuel
your body that are fat-tastic!**

Vegan & Vegetarian Friendly

GOJI BERRY SEED MIX

—

Ingredients
20 portions

100g goji berries
100g chia seeds
100g cacao nibs
100g pistachio nuts
Zest of 1 lemon

This is one of my favourite 'topper' recipes as it can be added to cereal, rice, potatoes and fruit. It provides a great range of nutritionally dense ingredients and you can modify it depending on what you have in your cupboards. The main things to remember is only make enough to last a week because once the seeds are milled the fats start to oxidise and will lose some of their quality; the seeds need to be milled otherwise they pass through the digestive system mainly undigested.

Method

This is a super simple recipe: just add all of the ingredients into a blender and give it a good blast, then store in an airproof container away from direct sunlight. Consume within a week.

Nutritional Breakdown

MACRO STATS	PER 100g	PER 20g SERVING (TWO TABLESPOONS)
CALORIES	*471*	*94.2*
CARBOHYDRATE	*28.5g*	*5.7g*
PROTEIN	*16.6g*	*3.32g*
FAT	*32.3g*	*6.46g*

Vegan & Vegetarian Friendly

HOMEMADE PISTACHIO NUT BUTTER

Ingredients
12 portions

200g shelled pistachio nuts (kernels)
45g light coconut oil

This is a real favourite with the riders – both Rigoberto Urán and Michael Woods always ask me to make it for them. The great thing with homemade nut butter is you can add extra tasty and nutritious items like goji berries or cacao nibs. I like to use pistachio kernels because these nuts have a great fat profile and are high in protein, but you can experiment with other tree nuts.

Method
Add the nuts and coconut oil to a powerful blender and mix until smooth; keep in a sterilised a jar with an airtight lid.

Nutritional Breakdown

MACRO STATS	PER 100g	PER 20g SERVING
CALORIES	*625*	*125.6*
CARBOHYDRATE	*7g*	*1.4g*
PROTEIN	*16.3g*	*3.26g*
FAT	*59.4g*	*11.88g*

Vegan & Vegetarian Friendly

SMASHED AVOCADO BREAKFAST

Ingredients
1 portion

½ a ripe avocado
¼ red onion approx.
15ml (one tbsp.) lime juice
Fresh coriander
Hot pepper sauce or a fresh red chilli

This is a brilliant staple of mine. I've even noticed a lot of cafés and even discount pub chains offering variants of it on toast as a vegan breakfast option.

Method

Cut the avocado in half; remove the stone and scoop out the flesh into a bowl. Finely chop and add the onion and lime juice and mash with the back of a fork. Season well with salt and pepper and finish with coriander leaves and chopped red chilli or hot pepper sauce to taste; serve with toast or as a side.

Nutritional Breakdown

MACRO STATS	PER 100g
CALORIES	*150*
CARBOHYDRATES	*3g*
PROTEIN	*1.5g*
FAT	*14.6g*

Vegetarian Friendly

PERFECT FLAX SEED OIL SALAD DRESSING

—

Ingredients
2-3 servings

30ml (two tbsp.) flax oil
30ml (two tbsp.) balsamic vinegar
Juice of half a lemon
5g (one tsp.) chia seeds
5g (one tsp.) sesame seeds

I don't think that we should just use dressings for salad as I will often use a dressing like this as a snack with some fresh homemade bread or to accompany roasted or griddled asparagus. This particular dressing is a favourite of mine. Flax seed oil is a massive provider of the essential oil alpha-linlolenic acid. It is a little bitter but the balsamic vinegar and lemon juice provide a nice sweet and sour balance to it. I have included some mashed seeds that enhance the nutritional value and also provide a nutty texture. You can also include some fresh herbs such as coriander.

Method
Use an old fashioned mortar and pestle to smash up the seed mix with the oil and balsamic vinegar, and then give it a good shake or blitz it in a blender.

Nutritional Breakdown

MACRO STATS	PER 100g	PER 20g SERVING
CALORIES	*480*	*96*
CARBOHYDRATES	*7.6g*	*1.52g*
PROTEIN	*3.9g*	*0.78g*
FAT	*48.2g*	*9.64g*

CARBOHYDRATES

—

When it comes to performance, carbohydrate is the king of fuels!

- CHAPTER 3 -
CARBOHYDRATES

—

Unlike with proteins and fats, if you're following a plant-based diet, there should be no real issues with you obtaining enough of the right sorts of carbohydrates to fuel your cycling. Given the high bulk of a typical plant-based diet, the only potential pitfall is ensuring that your food is delivering enough energy at the right times. However, even this shouldn't be too much of a concern – and we'll discuss it further in Chapter 6 (from p152) when we look at energy balance. It is still important to look at carbohydrates though, as no book on performance nutrition – plant-based or not – would be complete without a detailed examination of them.

> "For performance on the bike – carbohydrate is king"

As we've seen in Chapter 2 (from p48), when examining fat adaptive training and ketogenic diets, there has been a largely ill-founded movement away from carbohydrates as the number one endurance macronutrient. The realisation of the importance of both fats and protein to endurance performance has been genuinely revolutionary but, as with many things, some people took it a bit too far. The bottom line is – when it comes to performance on the bike – carbohydrate is king. If you fail to give your body enough carbohydrate, unless you're riding at a very easy pace, you'll come to a grinding halt. Thankfully we are now seeing more balance in the nutritional advice given and a re-examination of the best ways to optimise carbohydrate intake for performance.

Although, as a plant-based cyclist, you may have to devote more thought and attention to your protein and fat intake, it's essential – for the sake of your cycling performance – that you don't just assume you'll be getting your carbohydrates correct. Also, as I've stated earlier, a plant-based diet doesn't miraculously guarantee a healthy diet. This particularly applies to processed and manufactured foods; of which there's an ever-expanding range available to people following plant-based diets. Yes, they can be great and convenient but, whenever possible you should opt for unrefined and unprocessed whole foods. The main reason for this is that

Unprocessed carbohydrates can be a good source of vitamins, too

processing and refining, although tending to preserve the energy value of foods, strip out much of their nutrients. With carbohydrates, although refined ones definitely play important roles in on the bike and recovery nutrition, outside of those contexts you should generally be looking for less refined options, such as brown rice and whole grain bread and pasta. Whole grains do not only provide energy through carbohydrate but

also the B vitamins the body requires to metabolise the energy. I have met athletes who were consuming large volumes of processed carbohydrates but were becoming deficient with vitamins such as thiamin.

UNDERSTANDING CARBOHYDRATES

—

Carbohydrates exist in the form of sugars and starches. All carbohydrates are simply one or many simple sugars, known as monosaccharides, linked together.

Table sugar, or sucrose, is composed of two monosaccharides, glucose and fructose, and is referred to as a disaccharide.

Monosaccharide & Disaccharide

 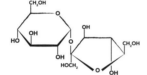

Monosaccharide (glucose)   *Disaccharide (sucrose)*

Lactose ('milk sugar') is also a disaccharide. A complex carbohydrate (a polysaccharide) for example maltodextrin, which is found in many sports drinks, is a chain of multiple monosaccharides. As we've already seen with both proteins and fats, our bodies are essentially production lines that take in complex molecules, dissemble them down to their constituent parts or building blocks and then use, store or reassemble them as required.

Polysaccharide

Polysaccharide (amylose starch)

This process is no different for carbohydrates, with the breakdown of polysaccharides beginning in the mouth via the chewing process and the action of the enzyme salivary amylase. In the stomach, acid stops the action of the salivary amylase but once in the small intestine, pancreatic amylase breaks down polysaccharides into disaccharide. Specific

"All carbohydrates are one or many simple sugars, linked"

enzymes (lactase, sucrase and maltase) then break the disaccharides down into their constituent monosaccharides; most importantly glucose as this is the body's preferred fuel. The glucose can be absorbed into the bloodstream to be used or stored. Lactose intolerance is fairly common in the adult population. This is because they either produce insufficient amounts of lactase or none at all. This is not an issue for a plant-based diet because lactose is solely found in milk and dairy.

In the case of refined cane sugar, table sugar sometimes uses bone char in its processing. So although sugar is plant-based it is not always vegan; the good news, however, is that there are an increasing number of vegan sugars on the market which aren't made using bone char, as well as suitable-for-vegans cane sugar alternatives from beet and cocount.

You should aim to take on 0.5-1g/ kg of bodyweight of carbs per hour

*Lower GI foods, such as quinoa,
are great for slow-release energy*

- THE GLYCEMIC INDEX (GI) -
Quick & slow carbs

The rate at which consumed carbohydrates get into your blood can be measured and is quantified by a scale known as the Glycemic Index (GI). The reference point of this scale is pure glucose, which has a value of 100. The scale was derived from experimental studies in which subjects were fasted overnight, fed 100g of pure glucose and the response in their blood glucose level monitored. With this baseline, they were then fed other foods, which delivered 100g of carbohydrate and the time taken to see the same blood response measured. This was then compared to their response to pure glucose and expressed as a percentage of it.

So, foods with a higher GI value are absorbed and available far more quickly. This is great if you're on the bike or looking for a fast acting recovery food. White rice, mashed potatoes and obviously energy gels and sports drinks will all have a high GI. For pre-exercise and the majority of meals, you should be looking for foods with a more moderate GI as the energy release will be more gradual. Porridge oats, quinoa and most whole grain products typically have lower GI values. Incidentally, if you're looking to drop some weight, definitely err towards lower GI carbohydrate sources. They'll not only keep you feeling fuller for longer but, as they result in less of a blood sugar spike, the insulin response is far lower and so less will be stored as fat. I've worked with riders with whom, by not necessarily reducing total carbohydrate intake but by switching to lower GI carbs – and so effectively changing distribution – weight loss has been facilitated.

It's important to remember that GI is not an indicator of the quality of the food, only its potential absorption rates. Also it is worth noting that if fat is included in the meal, this can significantly reduce the GI of the food.

For further information see the carbohydrate exchange list at the end of the chapter (on pages 99-101).

Not all carbohydrates found in food are digestible and usable as energy by humans. Plant cellulose is a non-digestible starch found in fruit and vegetables. That said, this fibre does play a vital role in maintaining gut health and is an essential component in a healthy and balanced diet. There are two main types of fibre: soluble and insoluble. Insoluble helps to form the bulk of the stool and soluble acts as a lubricant to keep the stool soft. Foods such as oats are great sources of soluble fibre and wholemeal bread the insoluble. We'll look more at both the importance of fibre and our gut fauna in Chapter 5 (which starts on p124).

Once in the bloodstream, glucose can be used immediately for energy or stored for later use. Normal blood glucose level is around 3.5-5.5mmol/l but depending on eating and exertion, this can fluctuate. For example, after a big meal it'll go up and, during a hard ride, it can drop. Blood glucose level is controlled by the hormone insulin, which is secreted by beta cells in the pancreas. The beta cells constantly monitor blood glucose level and, if they sense it's too high, release insulin. This instructs cells to take in the glucose and use what they need. For diabetics, who lack insulin, this doesn't happen and their blood glucose level can rise dangerously high. Any excess glucose is then converted to glycogen and stored in the skeletal muscles and liver and, once this is full, is converted to and stored as fat; this is also controlled by insulin. As the blood glucose level drops, the beta cells sense this and slow or cease insulin secretion. If blood glucose level drops too low, alpha cells in the pancreas sense this

and secrete glucagon. This signals your liver and muscles to release their stored glycogen back into your bloodstream. This process of balancing happens constantly in the body and maintains optimum blood glucose levels.

What's Happening When We Bonk?

So, if your body is constantly monitoring and manipulating your blood glucose level to keep it just right, why do you bonk on rides? More specifically, along with your legs failing you, why do you get that lightheaded sensation and lose your ability to focus and concentrate?

One of the main reasons that carbohydrates are so crucial is that the brain can only generally function on glucose. Your brain can use up to 100g of carbohydrate per day, which is the equivalent of about four or five bananas! In extreme situations, such as during starvation, our body can derive glucose for the brain from protein. The protein is broken into amino acids, which are then converted to glucose through a process called 'gluconeogenesis' in the liver. The source of this protein can be from food but, if this isn't available, the body will plunder its own lean tissue. This is why if a person is on a carbohydrate or calorie restricted diet, they have to ensure adequate protein to help protect lean muscle. However, obtaining energy from non-carbohydrate sources is a fairly slow and laborious process. If you're riding hard, there's simply not time, your working muscles are burning through carbs at a rate of knots and your blood glucose level crashes. In this 'starvation' state your body will also synthesise ketones from fat that the brain can use as energy as well

"Glucose can be used immediately for energy or stored"

If you feel a bonk coming on, back right off, and take a gel to reboot

but again, this doesn't happen fast enough when you're riding hard.

You might ask, what about our stored glycogen? Well, between your liver and skeletal muscles you can store about 400g worth of carbohydrate as glycogen and this represents approximately 2000kcals of energy. Although that might sound a lot,

if you're cycling hard, you could easily be getting through 1000kcals or more each hour. So, on a long ride, even with contributions from fat and from consumed carbohydrates, this store can easily become exhausted. Don't forget, the harder you ride, the more reliant the body is on carbohydrates. Once most of us are riding at an intensity where maintaining a conversation starts to become difficult, the

Riding hard can quickly deplete your glycogen stores

energy contribution from fat will be minimal. Once your glycogen stores are depleted, you're relying on ingested carbohydrates and, even with modern sports nutrition products and training, it's often not enough to keep up with the demand. As a result, blood glucose level plummets and, as your brain is starved of its preferred fuel, those all too familiar sensations of a bonk kick in.

- MOUTH RINSING -

Over the last few years a number of studies have shown that you don't even need to ingest carbohydrates for it to have a beneficial effect on performance. Carbohydrate rinsing is where you wash your mouth out with a 6% carbohydrate solution, which essentially tricks your body into performing better. It works by sensors in the mouth detecting the carbohydrates and sending signals to the pleasure and reward centres of the brain, saying there's more energy on the way. This gives you both a mental lift and gives a green light for our body to utilise any remaining energy stores.

From a practical perspective, it's worth trying as a final boost before a short time trial or track race or, on a longer ride, at the foot of a big climb. Also, it's a strong reason to always have that final gel or swig of energy drink, even though you might be near the end of the ride. There might not be time for it to be digested and absorbed but just that sweet hit in your mouth could help you get to the finishing line.

A great example of this was Chris Froome in the 2013 Tour de France. On the second ascent of Alpe d'Huez, Chris put in a big effort to drop Alberto Contador – and that probably pushed him over the edge. You could see it happening. He looked at his legs, as if he was asking them what was going on, and he came to a near standstill. He would have still had some muscle glycogen left but the high intensity he was riding at would have caused his blood sugar to suddenly drop and his brain would have initiated shutdown. Fortunately he had Richie Porte riding with him and, despite incurring a 20-second penalty for taking food within the final 20kms, the two gels that he fetched for Chris from the team car saved the day. There's no doubt in my mind that, without those gels, his losses would have been far more than 20 seconds. After the stage, some people questioned this decision, saying that at that point in the race, the gels had no time to act and were a waste of time. However, just that sweetness in his mouth and on his tongue would have stimulated his brain and allowed more glucose to be released from his liver.

Mouth rinsing 'fools' your body into releasing stored glucose

CARBOHYDRATE REQUIREMENTS

———

Unlike when we discussed protein, it's far harder with carbohydrates to give a hard and fast recommendation for how much you need each day. The reason why we can't be as prescriptive about carbohydrates is because of their primary role being fuelling. Simply put, the amount you need each day will vary massively on your training load and the intensity of it. Going back to the much used car analogy, you'll need a lot more fuel if you're driving all day than if your car is sat on the drive!

Cycling is unusual as an endurance sport as refuelling on the bike is relatively easy to do. It's zero impact, which allows easier digestion than the constant jarring of running; you can use your gears to manage intensity and the fact that you've got bottles, jersey pockets and – in the case of pro racers – supporting vehicles and staff, mean you can enjoy and digest a veritable picnic on the bike.

We'll discuss on-the-bike fuelling more thoroughly and with practical recommendations and recipes in Chapter 8 (starting on p190); but for now, as with overall carbohydrate intake, it's impossible to give hard and fast recommendations due to the effects of exercise duration and intensity.

A buzz phrase in sports nutrition currently is carbohydrate periodisation, which in simple terms just means adapting your carbohydrate intake to the training you're actually doing, so fuelling your sessions. In practice this is not a

new concept as, for years, riders have eaten more or less carbohydrates depending on the training they were doing – it's now just more structured and monitored. One of the things I often find with riders at all levels though, is that they tend to not eat enough during hard training but eat too much in easy training or on rest days.

On any ride over 90 minutes in duration, you should be looking to take on between 0.5-1g/kg/hour. The key though is to eat early, little and often. Right from the start of any long ride, you should be aiming to eat something every 20-30 minutes – don't wait until you feel hungry as you're not eating for that moment but rather for 15-30km further down the road.

The lower end of this scale – about 40g per hour for an 80kg rider, which might equate to 500ml of typical sports drink mixed at 6% and half an energy bar – would be okay for 90-120 minutes of riding at a steady pace. But if you're going longer and harder – especially if including a lot of climbing – you'd be looking to fuel towards the upper end of this range.

For post-ride recovery, again length and intensity of ride are the determining factors as they will govern how depleted you'll be. For 90-120 minutes of steady riding, you'd be looking at 1g/kg but, after a long and hard day in the saddle, that would rise to 1.5g/kg. However this requirement will be affected by when you are training again. If you are training the next day this is critical to ensure adequate metabolic recovery, but if you have a rest day it is less important.

On rest days, your carbohydrate requirements will be determined by your upcoming rides on subsequent days and by whether or not you're looking to lose weight. If you're not looking to lose weight or you have a big ride the next day, you should be looking to consume about the same as on a ride day but without the on the bike and recovery food. You're trying to recover and replenish your body's glycogen stores and that takes carbohydrates. If you are trying to lose some weight though, drop your carbohydrate intake by about 25% on rest days. However, be aware that this may compromise your training the next day and you'll need to weigh up the costs and benefits of this. In general, if you're training or racing hard, that's not the time to be trying to lose weight.

> "What to eat on the bike depends a lot on personal taste"

What to eat to obtain your carbohydrates on the bike depends a lot on personal taste and you need to experiment in training and find what works best for you. 'Real food', such as rice cakes, energy bars and bananas are slow burn like coal and will release energy gradually but continually over time. Gels and sports drinks are more like firelighters: they give a sudden but short-lived burst of energy.

In general, you should look to have a combination of fast and slow burn fuel for fuelling a long ride or race. Often the course profile will determine when and what to eat and I'll spend time with riders looking at a race route, identifying feeding opportunities.

For example, on a mountainous stage, the valley floor is a good time to take on slow burn real food and then, as the race intensity hots up going into and onto a climb, they'll switch to gels. Once over the top of the climb, unless they're having to push the descent, this can be another opportunity to take on more slow burn fuel.

The Spring Classics throw up a real challenge for fuelling, however. The racing is always full on, the roads are narrow and poorly surfaced and the riders are often wearing winter gloves, making dealing with real food tricky. In this situation, they'll rely almost exclusively on what they get from their bottles and gels. It's not unusual to see riders getting through 12 gels or more during the course of one of those brutal races.

Another issue with eating on the bike is gastric distress, feeling bloated and not being able to process fuel. Gut health plays a massive part in this and we look at this key area in Chapter 5 (starting on p124). Riding intensity plays a role too: if you're riding hard, blood flow to your working muscles will be prioritised and the blood supply to your digestive system effectively shut off. This means any food in your digestive tract will just sit there and, any additional food you try to eat, will just sit on top of it. However, it is possible to 'train' your digestive system and, if you practice and refine your fuelling strategies in training, your body will learn to tolerate fuelling at higher intensities. Finally, occasionally you'll see riders panic-eating, maybe because they've started to feel weak or a bit lightheaded. This never works out well, as, during exercise, there's a ceiling on the amount of carbohydrates you can process. Exceed this and, at best, it'll just sit in your stomach but your body might just get rid of it by making you sick. If you do start to feel weak or under fuelled, back your pace right off, go for some 'fast burn' fuel, such as a gel, and hopefully you'll recover. Even if you're just heading out for a steady ride, it's always worth slipping a couple of gels into your jersey. They can bail you out if you run out of food, if the ride drags on or if some mates turn up and the pace is a little more brisk than expected.

The Evolution Of Sports Drinks
In the 2018 Giro d'Italia, Chris Froome's epic solo race-winning ride on Stage 19 was largely credited to nutritional strategy and, in particular, a new generation of carbohydrate drinks that can efficiently deliver maximal amounts of carbohydrates even when working hard. Sports drinks have evolved massively over the years and, in particular, these latest generations are especially exciting. However, saying that – for steadier paced riding, especially on hot days – a 50/50 mix of pineapple juice and water with a pinch of salt is still hard to beat and easy on the wallet!

One of the key stages in the evolution of modern energy drinks was a gaining in understanding of multi-substrate fuelling. Maltodextrin is a long chain carbohydrate that's comprised of multiple glucose molecules. It's great in sports drinks because the digestive system sees each string of glucose molecules as a single particle so you can take more in. However, once the maltodextrin is broken down into glucose, the body's glucose channels soon become saturated, limiting the amount of energy you can absorb from it. The solution is to add

fructose into the mix – hence multi-substrate. As fructose is absorbed on different channels than glucose, uptake can be maximised.

However, if you make sports drinks too concentrated – typically above about 6% – they're usually poorly tolerated and can lead to gastric distress, especially in the quantities that a hard riding cyclist will consume it. It's not just the carbohydrate concentrations that are an issue; additional ingredients to enhance palatability can also contribute to problems. For a number of years with elite athletes, I have used very simple carbohydrate drinks with concentrations up to 20% but these have not been commercially available. Most commercially available sports drinks, when mixed correctly, will only typically deliver about 20g of carbohydrates in every 500ml bottle. This necessitates additional fuel, fine on a steady ride, not so easy in a full-on race.

Some of the latest generation of sports drinks – which I've been involved with the development of for over the last few years – uses hydrogel technology. By adding a gelling agent that's derived from seaweed, when the drink hits the stomach's acid it encapsulates the carbohydrates, making them tolerable at far higher concentrations. When released into the alkaline environment of the gut, the gel breaks down and the carbohydrates can be absorbed. These drinks can deliver an incredible 80g of carbohydrates per 500ml bottle and are incredibly easy on the stomach. This means, even during the hardest races, riders can fuel from their bottles alone; this is incredibly useful during the high octane, poor conditions and long distances associated with the Spring Classics.

*Nutrition aided Chris Froome
towards his historic Giro win*

- SUMMARY -
CARBOHYDRATES

———

Carbohydrates Are King
Becoming well fat-adapted and developing your ability to utilise fat as a fuel is a key component of endurance fitness. However, unless you solely want to focus on very long and very steady riding, don't buy into fat adaptation and ketogenic evangelism. For any level of performance – even riding a sportive at a decent pace – you're going to need carbohydrates. Shun carbohydrates and you'll never reach your cycling potential.

Don't Take Carbohydrates For Granted
In all likelihood, if you're following either a vegetarian or vegan diet, you'll probably be consuming a decent amount of carbohydrates as most plant-based foods tend to contain some. Also, with meat removed from a diet, carbohydrate intake typically rises. The relatively high bulk of a plant-based diet can make getting enough energy difficult though, especially when training or racing hard. If you notice your performance dropping, poor recovery or unexpected weight loss, check your intake.

Beat The Bonk
If you're experiencing the physical and cognitive sensations of a bonk, you've got either your fuelling or pacing – or both – wrong. Nail your fuelling and pacing strategies in training and you'll also develop your body's capability to take on and utilise fuel at higher intensities. If you do start to get the telltale signs of an imminent bonk, back right off, take on a gel and reboot your system.

Fuel Your Riding & Recovery
Tailor your carbohydrate intake to the riding you're doing and whether you're looking to lose or maintain weight. Remember, you're not only eating for that moment but also to recover from the ride you've just done and your upcoming rides. If you're fuelling well on the bike and after rides and are not looking to lose weight, you should be aiming for fairly consistent day-to-day carbohydrate intake.

Carbohydrate Spares Protein
On a plant-based diet, it's possible that your protein intake may be a bit on the low side. Having sufficient carbohydrate will help to protect your lean muscle tissue and mean that the precious protein you have eaten can be used for growth, repair and recovery.

Let The Route Dictate Your Fuelling
Follow the lead of the pros and study route profiles to plan and adapt your fuelling strategy. Take advantage of easier sections, such as valley roads and non-technical descents, to eat slower burning real food. Opt for gels and other fast burn fuels on climbs or if the pace hots up. If you've got a long and hard ride when – due to the weather conditions, your clothing or the terrain – taking on real food might be tricky, try out some of the new generation of hydrogel drinks.

"Don't sit on the fence, you either like bananas or you don't"

*Each flapjack (recipe on p232)
gives around 30g of carbohydrates*

CARBOHYDRATE EXCHANGE LIST

FOOD PORTIONS CONTAINING 50g OF CARBOHYDRATE	APPROXIMATE WEIGHT (GRAMS/OUNCE)	HANDY MEASURE	GI (PURE GLUCOSE = 100)
BREAKFAST CEREALS			
PORRIDGE (MADE WITH WATER & SWEETENED NON-DAIRY MILK)	500g/20oz	2 large bowls	**50**
WEETABIX	75g/3oz	3-4 biscuits	**75**
SHREDDED WHEAT	75g/3oz	3 biscuits	**70**
SHREDDIES	75g/3oz	1 large bowl	**65**
BRAN FLAKES	75g/3oz	1 large bowl	**70**
CORN FLAKES	50g/2oz	1 large bowl	**80**
MUESLI	75g/3oz	1 medium bowl	**50**
ALL-BRAN	50g/2oz	1 large bowl	**60**
CEREALS & GRAINS/PSEUDO-GRAINS			
QUINOA (RAW)	80g/3oz	½ cup	**35**
AMARANTH (RAW)	80g/3oz	1/2 cup	**35**
PASTA - WHITE OR WHOLEWHEAT (COOKED)	225g/9oz	8 tablespoons	**40**
RICE WHITE (COOKED)	175g/7oz	4 tablespoons	**65**
RICE BASMATI (COOKED)	175g/7oz	4 tablespoons	**50**
TINNED SPAGHETTI IN TOMATO SAUCE	400g/16oz	1 large can	**70**
PEARLED SPELT (RAW)	80g/3oz	½ cup	**35**
PULSES			
BAKED BEANS	325g/13oz	7 tablespoons	**55**
SWEETCORN	300g/12oz	10 tablespoons	**60**
RED KIDNEY BEANS	300g/12oz	10 tablespoons	**50**
CHICKPEAS	275g/11oz	10 tablespoons	**40**

CARBOHYDRATE EXCHANGE LIST

FOOD PORTIONS CONTAINING 50g OF CARBOHYDRATE	APPROXIMATE WEIGHT (GRAMS/OUNCE)	HANDY MEASURE	GI (PURE GLUCOSE = 100)
POTATOES			
BOILED	300g/12oz	5 egg size	**60**
JACKET/SKIN	175g/7oz	1 medium	**50**
SWEET POTATO	175g/7oz	1 medium	**40**
MASHED	325g/13oz	5 scoops	**70**
ROAST	200g/8oz	4 small	**75**
CRISPS	100g/4oz	4 packets	**55**
LOW FAT CRISPS	75/3oz	3 packets	**50**
BAKERY PRODUCTS			
WHITE BREAD	100g/4oz	3-4 slices	**70**
WHOLEMEAL BREAD	125g/5oz	3-4 slices	**60**
ROLLS	100g/4oz	2	**70**
PITTA BREAD	100g/4oz	1 large	**60**
NAAN BREAD	100g/4oz	2 mini	**50**
RYE BREAD (PUMPERNICKEL)	100g/4oz	3 large slices	**50**
TORTILLA WRAPS	100g/4oz	1 ½ medium slices	**65**
CRUMPETS	125g/5oz	3	**69**
CURRANT BUNS/TEACAKES	100g/4oz	1-2	**90**
FRUIT SCONES	100g/4oz	2	**50**
MALT LOAF	100g/4oz	2-3 slices	**72**
BAGELS	75/3oz	1	**70**
CEREAL BARS AND DESSERTS			
JORDANS FRUSLI (FRUIT & NUT)	80g/3oz	2 ½ bars	**75**
JORDANS ORIGINAL CRUNCHY	80g/3oz	2 ½ bars	**75**
TRACKER (NUT)	80g/3oz	3 bars	**75**
NUTRIGRAIN BARS	70g/3oz	2 bars	**65**

FOOD PORTIONS CONTAINING 50g OF CARBOHYDRATE	APPROXIMATE WEIGHT (GRAMS/OUNCE)	HANDY MEASURE	GI (PURE GLUCOSE = 100)
FRUITS			
APPLES	425g/17oz	4 medium	**40**
ORANGES	625g/25oz	4 medium	**40**
PEARS	525g/21oz	3 medium	**40**
BANANAS	225g/9oz	2 large	**55**
APRICOTS (DRIED)	150g/6oz	20	**30**
DATES (DRIED)	100g/4oz	7	**100**
FIGS (DRIED)	100g/4oz	5	**60**
RAISINS	75g/3oz	3 tablespoons	**65**
GRAPES	325g/13oz	60	**50**
PEACHES IN JUICE	500g/13oz	1 large can	**50**
PINEAPPLE IN JUICE	400g/16oz	1 large can	**60**
APRICOTS IN JUICE	400g/16oz	1 ½ large cam	**65**
CRACKERS			
OATCAKES	75g/3oz	6	**57**
RYVITA	75g/3oz	9	**65**
CRACKERS	75g/3oz	10	**65**
RICE CAKES	75g/3oz	10	**70**
DAIRY FOODS			
RICE PUDDING (LOW FAT)	325g/13oz	1 can	**60**
ICE CREAM	225g/9oz	4 scoops	**50**
SUGAR/PRESERVES			
TABLE SUGAR – WHITE OR BROWN	50g/2oz	12 level teaspoons	**95**
JAM	75g/3oz	9 level teaspoons	**60**
HONEY	75g/3oz	9 level teaspoons	**50**
SYRUP	75g/3oz	9 level teaspoons	**75**

CARBOHYDRATE EXCHANGE LIST

Reference: McCance R.A., Widdowson, E.M. (1991). The Composition of Foods, RSC. Crawley, H. (1988). Food Portion Sizes. H.M.S.O. Glycemic Index Website. www.glycemicindex.com University of Sydney.

KEY *25g = 1 oz*   *25ml = 1 fl oz*

MICRONUTRIENTS & SUPPLEMENTS

—

Get set to meet your new best friends:
the 'Go', 'Grow' and 'Glow' nutrients.

- CHAPTER 4 -

MICRONUTRIENTS & SUPPLEMENTS

—

Proteins, fats and carbohydrates are collectively known as the macronutrients. As we've seen they're primarily involved with energy production, growth and repair. In simple terms, they can be thought of as the 'Go And Grow Nutrients'. Micronutrients are the vitamins and minerals and I consider these as the 'Glow Nutrients'. We need these for health, wellbeing and smooth running of the body – but only in relatively small amounts.

When you think about the range of foods that are available when following a plant-based diet – such as fruits and vegetables and nutrient-dense nuts, seeds and pulses – you'd think there'd be no issues with micronutrient intake. However it's important to remember that a plant-based diet doesn't guarantee a healthy diet and, especially if you're focussing on macronutrient intake to fuel your training and recovery, or tend to be reliant on processed or convenience foods, you could be missing out on some key micronutrients. Also, there are a number of micronutrients that can often be deficient in a plant-based diet and may require special attention.

Here we'll look in general at what vitamins and minerals are, then focus in on the ones that might need special attention. For each of these micronutrients we'll examine its role, why you might not be getting enough of it, the possible implications and symptoms of not consuming high enough levels and how to remedy the situation.

We'll then move onto the related subject of supplementation, for heath and performance. It's worth noting that, especially if you're new to or transitioning to a plant-based diet or are experiencing fatigue, poor recovery from training or unexpectedly poor performance, then blood testing to check the levels of a number of key micronutrients is strongly recommended. In fact, for all cyclists who are serious about performance, it's arguably as important as getting your bike serviced.

There are a number of companies who offer postal services, making it both convenient and affordable. We'll look more at blood testing in Chapter 6 (from p152) including monitoring your health and diet.

⟶

UNDERSTANDING MICRONUTRIENTS & SUPPLEMENTS

—

Vitamins are a collection of complex carbon based molecular compounds that have a wide range of physiological functions. They are classified into two groups based on their solubility: fat-soluble and water-soluble vitamins.

Fat-soluble vitamins (A, D, E and K) can be readily stored in the body so that they are available when needed. But if consumed to excess they can build up to harmful levels.

Water-soluble vitamins (B group and C) are not generally stored, and any excess intake is excreted in urine. They can still, however, be toxic in excessive amounts.

Along with vitamins, we also need to consume small amounts of inorganic compounds that contain metal and non-metal ions. These ions are often referred to as minerals. An example of such an inorganic compound is table salt, which contains both sodium chloride and potassium iodide. These compounds dissolve in the gut, releasing ions that are crucial both to cell function and water balance in the body.

Some minerals are required in relatively large amounts (over 100 milligrams) and these are referred to as the macrominerals. There are seven of them: calcium, phosphorus, chlorine, potassium, sulphur, sodium and magnesium.

The microminerals, iron, copper, zinc and fluorine, are needed in milligram amounts. The trace minerals include iodine, selenium, vanadium, chromium, manganese, cobalt, nickel, molybdenum and tin and are needed in microgram amounts.

All of these minerals are essential to optimal body function and performance.

> "Vitamins have a wide range of physiological functions"

Many soy milks are fortified with vitamin B12

MICRONUTRIENTS TO CONSIDER

———

Following a plant-based diet does not mean you will be deficient in the following micronutrients but you should be aware of the possibility so you can pay special attention to these.

Vitamin B12

With vitamin B12 typically coming from meat-based sources, obtaining enough when following a plant-based diet can be an issue. The main roles of vitamin B12 in the body is in the formation of red blood cells and carbohydrate metabolism so its importance to endurance athletes is obvious. Typically, a deficiency in vitamin B12 is due to low dietary intake but this isn't always the case; some people lack what's known as the 'intrinsic factor', a glycoprotein that's necessary for the absorption of vitamin B12, but this is a relatively rare condition.

When intake or absorption are low, red blood cells don't form properly, becoming large, misshaped and known as megaloblastic. This results in a condition known as pernicious anaemia, which is characterised by low energy and poor recovery from training.

Fortunately many foods – such as bread, cereals, savoury spreads and non-dairy milk – are fortified with vitamin B12 and, as long as enough of these are consumed, you shouldn't have a problem. Where I have seen cases of people following plant-based diets having low vitamin B12 levels, it's usually because they've been too zealous in trying

to follow a 'natural' diet and have actively avoided fortified foods.

Another point to consider about vitamin B12 is that, if you have a good store of it in your body, it can take a surprising amount of time of not eating enough of it for your levels to fall to sub-optimal levels. This means, especially if you're transitioning to a plant-based diet, low vitamin B12 levels can effectively creep up on you.

The current recommended nutrient intake for B12 for adults is 1.5µg per day (UK Government Dietary Recommendations, 2016); the US guidelines are slightly higher at 2.4µg. There are two forms of B12 supplements: cyanocobalamin and methylcobalamin. Cyanocobalamin is an inactive form and needs to be activated by an intrinsic factor; this is the form that is used in food fortification and most supplements. Methylcobalamin is an active form of B12 and does not require intrinsic factor; it is a lot more expensive and is not as commonly used.

Examples of plant-based vitamin B12-rich foods:

- Yeast extract spread e.g. *Marmite*
- Fortified soy milk
- Fortified yeast flakes
- Fortified cereals
- Fortified soya spread

Vitamin D

Vitamin D, specifically its active form vitamin D3, can rightly be thought of as being akin to a hormone due to the messenger roles it plays within the body. It's vital for bone health, immune function and for maintaining a healthy nervous system. It's also known as the 'sunshine vitamin' as, from sunlight, pigmentation in our skin is able to synthesise it. So, during the summer months, regardless of what you eat, if you're getting out on your bike regularly, you shouldn't have any issues. That said, we're starting to see a re-emergence of the childhood bone disease rickets, which is caused by vitamin D deficiency, especially in hot and sunny climates. The reason? Parents are protecting their children from the sun too much.

However, especially in the Northern Hemisphere, for at least six months of the year, there simply isn't the length and quality of sunlight for our bodies to produce enough vitamin D. This means we're more reliant on dietary sources and, as the primary sources are eggs and oily fish, this can be a problem if you're following a plant-based diet. In fact, even for people who do eat fish and eggs, maintaining adequate vitamin D levels during the winter is extremely difficult. So much so that the UK's National Health Service (NHS) current guidelines are that everyone should supplement their vitamin D intake during the winter months. If you're following a plant-based diet, you'll be lacking both from a sunlight and dietary perspective and so, some level of supplementation is definitely needed. When I followed a plant-based diet for 12 weeks, I started in late September and my blood profile showed normal vitamin D levels. However, by late December, when I repeated the blood test, the combination of a lack of sunlight exposure and the plant-based diet had caused my vitamin D levels to fall.

As with vitamin B12, for the cyclist, low levels of vitamin D are likely to manifest as low energy, poor recovery from and adaptation to training and also poor immune function. General lethargy and a lack of motivation can be an indicator of a number of deficiencies and the only way to be sure of the exact cause is a blood test. Vitamin D levels have become a standard marker that is measured with routine blood tests for professional cyclists. They tend to be measured about four times a year and we tend to find that about 30% of riders have low levels and require supplementation.

As a general recommendation though, especially though the winter months and if training hard, you should look to take a supplement delivering 4000iu of vitamin D every other day. The best form to take is vitamin D3 and, although there are vegan versions available, many are derived from sheep wool. Vitamin D2 is an alternative that will come from plant-based sources and will act as a precursor to D3 when ingested. However, as there is some loss during the conversion process, it will be necessary to take higher levels.

Examples of plant-based vitamin D-rich foods:

- Mushrooms, such as Portobello and regular white mushrooms; if these are exposed to sunlight, they naturally produce vitamin D
- Vitamin D2 fortified non-dairy milks
- Fortified tofu

Our skin synthesises vitamin D
directly from sunlight

*Japanese rice balls are a great
iodine-rich travel and bike snack*

Green beans are also a tasty way to get your idodine in

"Plant-based foods contain iodine but the amounts can be low"

Iodine

The mineral iodine is essential for healthy thyroid function and the production of the hormone thyroxine. Severe iodine deficiency can result in a swelling of the thyroid gland known as a goitre (also known as a 'goiter') but, before that stage, low levels will manifest in poor energy levels and potentially weight gain. The main dietary sources of iodine are from fish and other seafood and so can potentially be problematic if you're following a plant-based diet. However, many areas' water supplies have been fortified with iodine for a number of years. Also there are various seaweeds and seaweed-derived supplements that you can include in your diet and offer a great plant-based source of iodine.

A lot of plant-based foods contain iodine but the amounts can be low and is dependent on the soil quality. However the best plant food that is high in iodine is seaweed. One of the travel snack and on the bike options I make is based on Japanese rice balls wrapped in seaweed (see Chapter 7, p186, for the recipe).

Examples of plant-based iodine-rich foods:

- Seaweed
- Kelp (seaweed supplement)
- Kale
- Green beans
- Whole grains

Iron

Iron is one of the most important minerals for endurance athletes as, forming the 'haem' component of haemoglobin in our red blood cells, it's essential for the transport of oxygen throughout our body. Myoglobin, which is responsible for oxygen transport and transfer within our working muscles, is also iron-based.

Unfortunately if you consume a plant-based diet, the most readily available and easily absorbed food source of iron is meat. Although many plant-based foods are reasonably iron rich, it's not in a form that's so accessible to your body. Also, a number of phytochemical substances within plants, such as tannins, bind with iron in a process known as chelation and further lower absorbency. Also, if you're training or racing hard, your body's ability to absorb iron goes down; this is because when the body is stressed it produces a hormone called hepcidin which down regulates iron absorption. This is why, if I'm looking to raise the iron levels of a rider, I'll do so during lighter work periods or recovery blocks. For female riders, there's the additional concern of iron loss during menstruation, which can be significant. So, in short, if you're a hard riding cyclist, who's following a plant-based diet, especially if you're female, iron levels could be an issue.

As with the other micronutrient deficiencies previously described, the symptoms for low iron levels are typically fatigue, poor recovery from training and a drop-off in performance. Once again, I'll stress the importance of having a blood test to check where the issue lies and not to wait until you notice possible symptoms. I'd recommend having iron levels, as part of a general blood examination, checked every three to six months. When assessing iron – expressed as ferritin level –

it's important to bear in mind that the ideal range for athletes does differ to the typical normative range. In the normal population, above 20ng/ml is considered okay but, for endurance athletes, I'd be wanting to see levels well in excess of 60ng/ml.

As you'll see from the list on the following pages, there are some great plant sources of iron but, as previously mentioned, absorption from them won't be nearly as good as meat. There are however a couple of steps you can take to boost your iron intake from your food. The first is to use acidic dressings, such as vinegar and lemon juice, with iron rich greens. The acid oxidises the iron and makes it easier for your body to absorb. The second is to introduce iron into your food from your cookware. Stir frying in a traditional steel wok, not an expensive non-stick coated one, will significantly boost the iron content of your food. You can also get an 'Iron Fish' – literally a lump of iron shaped like a fish – which you pop in your cooking pot to raise iron levels.

Supplementation is also an option and, for serious cyclists following a plant-based diet, worth considering, especially if a blood test has shown low iron levels.

An iron fish in your cooking pot helps up your food's iron content

Hard racing can reduce your body's ability to absorb iron

Iron supplementation is something that I often prescribe to the professional riders I work with as, even those who eat meat, often present with low levels. There can be GI issues associated with iron supplementation, such as nausea and constipation, and the best way to prevent this is to spread the daily dose into a frequent small measures throughout the day. Dosage will vary depending on your blood profile and need but, for a general prophylactic dose, the 15mg typically found in many multi-mineral supplements suffices.

Examples of plant-based iron rich foods:

- Green leafy vegetables, especially spinach, remember Popeye!
- Dried fruit, especially apricots
- Nuts and milled seeds
- Fortified cereals
- Whole grains such as brown rice and quinoa

- IRON & ALTITUDE -

Altitude training has been a staple of top-level cyclists for a number of years. Altitude training blocks are used for two main reasons. One is to acclimatise to altitude in preparation for races that go high (the highest pass that the Tour de France has tackled is the Cime de la Bonette-Restefond at 2802m, which last featured in 2008). But the primary reason is for the blood boosting effect that altitude has on the body. In order to cope with the lower partial pressure of oxygen, the body produces more red blood cells. Upon returning to sea level, an athlete can expect to see a performance boost from the increased red blood cell count for 10-14 days. Altitude training camps will typically last two to three weeks and the most common protocol is for the riders to 'live high and train low'. This gives the greatest physiological adaptation but without compromising the quality of training they do. Obviously though, to produce more red blood cells, the body requires more iron and, if levels aren't optimum, the beneficial effects of the camp will be compromised and riders can even return weaker than when they left. So, we'll always make a point of loading the riders' iron levels before they go and also on their return.

More serious amateur riders are now emulating the pros and are either going on altitude training camps or are renting or buying altitude tents that allow them to 'sleep high' at home. However, even if you're not going on cycling specific trips to altitude, you might be spending a week or more at altitude on a ski trip and, if you don't pay attention to your iron levels, won't get the bonus boost to your riding and might even return home to find a dip in your performance.

Calcium

If you're a vegetarian who eats dairy then you won't have any issues with calcium intake but, if you're a vegan, it can be an issue. Calcium is important for bone health but also serves a number of other vital roles in the body. These include blood clotting and muscular contraction. Our bones are metabolically active tissues and act as our body's calcium reservoir and, if we're not taking in enough, it'll be leached from our bones compromising their density and strength. Like iron, there are plenty of plant-based foods that are fairly rich in calcium but, because of issues with chelation and absorption, the amount that actually is available to your body from them can be relatively low.

In the short term, a mild to moderate calcium deficiency probably wouldn't present any noticeable symptoms. However in the long term it can have serious implications for bone health, in particular bone density. This is particularly pertinent for cyclists as, with cycling being a non-weight bearing activity, this also can lead to issues with bone density.

Along with trying to eat calcium rich plant-based foods, again fortified foods can provide an easy solution. Many dairy free milk alternatives will be fortified with calcium. Supplementation is also an option and when I was following a plant-based diet, I opted to cover my bases with a combined calcium, zinc and magnesium supplement. I tend to recommend that cyclists consume about 1g of calcium per day and this can be challenging from food alone.

Examples of plant-based calcium rich foods:

- Fortified non-dairy milks
- Kale
- Tofu (when a calcium salt is used for setting)
- Blackstrap molasses
- Almonds
- Black beans

Zinc

The main dietary sources of zinc are animal-based and it's particularly abundant in seafood. However certain nuts and seeds are also fairly abundant in it and you should be looking to include plenty of these in your diet. Zinc is involved in immune function, metabolism and cellular repair and, although deficiencies are fairly rare, it's something to be aware of if you're following a plant-based diet. Symptoms will be fatigue, feeling run down and poor immunity, as with most of the other micronutrients we've discussed so, the only way to pin it to zinc would be to have a blood test. As I've previously mentioned, I took a combined supplement that included zinc just to ensure I was getting enough.

Examples of plant-based zinc rich foods:

- Most nuts
- Milled seeds, especially flax, pumpkin and sunflower
- Green leafy vegetables
- Wholemeal grains

SUPPLEMENTATION

——

We've already touched on supplementation when discussing protein in Chapter 1 (see p32, onwards), Omega-3 fats in Chapter 2 (see p48, onwards), and with reference to specific micronutrients earlier in this chapter. Although it is theoretically possible to obtain all the necessary nutrients from a plant-based diet without the use of supplements, with time pressure and the unpredictable nature of modern life, it can be very difficult. Factor in the additional stresses of your cycling training and racing and, maybe for some of you, making the change and adapting to a plant-based diet and the sensible use of some supplements as a safety net can be a good idea.

Multivitamin/Mineral

A common topic of debate and controversy is whether there's any need for or benefit to taking a broad spectrum multivitamin and mineral. My personal recommendation is: if you're transitioning to a plant-based diet, have any doubts about whether your diet is providing everything you need or just want that belt and braces reassurance, it's certainly not going to do any harm.

Use a vegan-friendly product that provides a broad spectrum of the vitamins and minerals and does not supply above the 100% RDA levels. There's no point in exceeding these levels and it could even be dangerous. Excess water soluble vitamins, such as vitamin C, will simply be excreted but fat soluble vitamins, A, D, E and K, can build up to toxic levels in the body. If you're also taking other supplements, such as those discussed earlier in the chapter for specific micronutrients, it's important to check that you're not doubling up on any doses.

- MY REGIME -

Below are the supplements I took when following a plant-based diet:

- Calcium, magnesium and zinc (combined): I had two tablets a day providing 666.6mg of calcium, 266.6mg of magnesium and 16.6mg zinc.
- Unflavoured vegan protein: 20g/day
- Vegan Omega-3 oil: 1g/day
- Iron: 15mg/day

Supplementation can be used as a 'belts and braces' tactic

Creatine can be used to maintain health or boost performance

ERGOGENICS

———

Ergogenics are the supplements that can supposedly improve your performance on the bike, tolerance to training and racing and your ability to recover. There are literally hundreds of substances with claimed performance benefits and you could easily write a whole book dedicated to analysing their use and efficacy alone. For our purpose here, we'll limit ourselves to the discussion of just three which are most relevant to a plant-based diet: creatine, beta alanine, and branched-chain amino acids (BCAAs).

Creatine

Creatine is used in the body to fuel short, up to about six-second, bouts of explosive activity. It's use as an ergogenic supplement first came about in strength, power and sprint sports, however its use has become more popular amongst cyclists, especially on the track.

Found predominately in beef, pork and fish, it can be difficult for cyclists eating a purely plant-based diet to maintain normal creatine levels; studies have confirmed this and you'd probably struggle to consume 1g/day. So, a low dose supplement (2g/day) can be a good idea. At this low dose, you won't experience the weight gain associated with more traditional and far higher dosage creatine-loading regimes but will maintain the levels that a meat eating cyclist would have. You should aim to take the creatine after training with your recovery drink as that will aid with absorption. I have used this low dose strategy with professional riders successfully.

In order to achieve an ergogenic effect, as opposed to simply levelling the creatine playing field with meat eating riders, you would probably need to up the dosage to 5g/day. This is still far less than strength, power and speed athletes would take but would only really be advantageous for track cyclists, shorter time trials or crit racers. If you're really focusing on a strength training block or are looking to increase lean weight, you should load for about a week taking four doses of 5g each day and then dropping back to a maintenance dose of 5g/day.

Originally creatine supplements were derived from shellfish but now they are predominately artificially synthesised and so are suitable for vegans.

Beta Alanine

This is one of the non-essential amino acids. A prominent Sports Bio-chemist, Dr Roger Harris from the UK's University of Chichester – who was also responsible for discovering the potential benefits of creatine – also studied the muscle buffer carnosine. He discovered that the limiting factor to carnosine levels in the body was the availability of one of its component parts: beta alanine. He found that by increasing beta alanine in the diet that you could increase the carnosine and improve the buffering in the muscle. This means you're able to better tolerate and recover from high intensity sprint efforts which raise cellular hydrogen ion concentration.

Beta alanine comes predominately from animal sources and turkey meat is particularly

Beta alanine boosts lactic buffering at high intensities

high in it. So, like creatine, cyclists following a plant-based diet might well struggle to obtain normal levels of it in their diet, let alone levels that would boost performance. Therefore, if you're looking to compete on the track or in other cycling disciplines requiring multiple sprint or high intensity efforts, its use is recommended.

I first used it with Team Pursuit riders in 2006 and now it's used almost universally by track riders. I see beta alanine more as a training aid than a competition boost. Especially if you are doing high intensity workouts with multiple sprint or supra-threshold efforts, it can help you push that bit harder and achieve more during the session.

Vegetarian beta alanine supplements are available on the market, and you should load for about four weeks taking 4g/day and then drop to a maintenance dose of 1g/day. Many riders do experience a tingling sensation after consuming beta alanine. This is completely harmless and it could be argued that this tangible physiological effect of taking the supplement increases its efficacy due to an enhanced placebo effect. If you don't like the tingling effect it can be reduced by taking it mixed with foods.

Branched-Chain Amino Acids (BCAAs)

This is a special group of amino acids that, as the name suggests, have a different structure to other amino acids. Examples of BCAAs include leucine, isoleucine and valine. Dairy, in particular whey protein, is high in BCAAs and these special amino acids, particularly leucine, can be of real benefit for cyclists as they have a positive effect on protein synthesis. Even though you can consume your basic nutritional requirements of BCAAs from a plant-based diet, during heavy training it may also be worth taking some additional BCAAs in the form of a supplement and happily there are now plant-based products on the market. I have been recently working with a pro plant-based cyclist and we have included a BCAA supplement in his diet – this has been moderate and only used in hard training periods. My suggestion is 2g of BCAAs with lunch and evening meal.

- TRUST YOUR SUPPLEMENTS -

Under the code of the World Anti-Doping Agency (WADA) an athlete takes full responsibility for what they put into their body. This is termed 'strict liability'. So, if you fail a test because of a contaminated supplement, that's no excuse and full sanctions will be taken. There have been many cases of top-level athletes being caught out in this way and received a doping violation. This can happen very easily as, in a lot of factories where nutritional products are made, they also make substances that contain these banned, but not illegal, contaminates.

If you're competing at national level or masters competition, there is a chance you could be drug tested. In theory, any rider with a racing license can also be tested at any time. You're responsible for ensuring that any supplements you may take are clean. The simplest way to do this and identify products that have been screened is to look for some guarantee or to check with the manufacturers that they have been batch tested. If in doubt, don't take it.

UNDERSTANDING VITAMINS & MINERALS

*If you don't like how it tastes,
eat it in something tasty*

- SUMMARY -
MICRONUTRIENTS & SUPPLEMENTS

Go & Grow Versus Glow

Proteins, fats and carbohydrates are collectively referred to as macronutrients and are responsible for energy production, growth and repair; you can think of them as the 'Go And Grow' nutrients. Vitamins and minerals, known as micronutrients are needed in far smaller amounts but are essential for health and general bodily function; they're the 'Glow' nutrients. Don't assume, just because you're eating a plant-based diet, that you'll be getting all of your 'Glow' nutrients.

Get Tested

There are a number of specific micronutrients that might be deficient in a plant-based diet but all tend to produce similar symptoms of fatigue, poor recovery, low immunity and performance drop-off. The only way to know for sure where your issue lies is from regular blood testing. There are a number of companies who offer remote testing services by post so there's really no excuse.

Cover Your Bases

Although an area of debate and some controversy, the use of certain supplements can provide you with a useful safety net and reassurance. When I followed a plant-based diet I adopted this approach and, especially if you're transitioning to such a diet or not confident that your food is providing adequate nutrients to support your training, it's certainly not going to do you any harm.

Levelling The Playing Field

If your racing and training involve regular high intensity or sprint efforts, such as for track cycling, there are two supplements you should consider to level the playing field with your meat eating competitors. Both creatine and beta alanine intake tends to be inadequate in a purely plant-based diet and this could have a negative effect on your performance.

If you race at high intensities,
supplements may work for you

MAINTAINING A HEATHLY DIGESTIVE SYSTEM

—

Don't accept digestive discomfort – there is a better, happier way!

- CHAPTER 5 -

MAINTAINING A HEALTHY DIGESTIVE SYSTEM

———

A common and slightly clichéd analogy used in many nutrition books is that you wouldn't put substandard fuel in your car and expect it to perform so, why would you expect it of your body? However I'd take this analogy further and say that there's no point in putting decent fuel in your car, or nutritious food in your body, if your fuel lines, your digestive system, are not clear, well maintained and able to get the most out of that fuel.

Plant-based diet or not, maintaining gut health is crucial for performance and is especially important for endurance athletes due to the strains they put on their bodies. When working as a clinical dietitian, much of my time was spent dealing with immune-compromised patients. Whether they were suffering from conditions such as cancer or HIV and AIDS, optimising their gut health

> "Maintaining gut health is crucial for endurance athletes"

was a key part of their treatment. Unless their gut health could be maintained, getting the necessary nutrients into them was extremely difficult. I found a similar situation with top-level cyclists, especially during hard training blocks and on three week Grand Tours. Unless their gut health could be maintained, they simply couldn't take in and process the fuel that they required. This explained the bloating, nausea and lack of energy many riders reported in the third week of Grand Tours and, in the dark old days of the sport, was one of the rationales behind using injectables, both legal and illegal. However by applying what I learned during my clinical practice, I found that, despite the massive stress on their systems, I was able to maintain the riders' gut health and function. This meant they could fuel better, recover better and ultimately ride better.

"Hang on, this isn't a hop!"

I've always prioritised making my patients' and athletes' guts as healthy and robust as possible and you should try to do the same. A lot of people have long term gastric issues that they learn to put up with and accept but these can often be significantly improved or even resolved. These issues can include bloating, reflux, excessive wind and constipation. In my clinical practice I have a growing number of clients referred for support around gut health issues.

It's important to gain an understanding of how nutrients get into the body and into our cells then how we use them. At the very start of the chain, all of our food is reliant on the sun and the energy it provides. This energy is absorbed by plants by the process of photosynthesis and is converted to carbohydrates, an available and usable energy source. The plants then use that energy to grow, forming proteins. Plants are packed with proteins, especially the legumes, which are really good at making protein, utilising special nodules in the roots that can actually 'fix' nitrogen directly from the air and soil.

So – whether you eat animal products or not – all of your energy and nutrients comes from the sun via plants. Thus, you could argue that we all eat a plant- or even a sun-based diet! We've cultivated plants for millennia and developed strains that give us the best possible yield and, by eating their nuts, seeds, stems, roots, leaves, fruiting bodies and even flowers, we can obtain all the nutrients we need.

→

DIGESTION

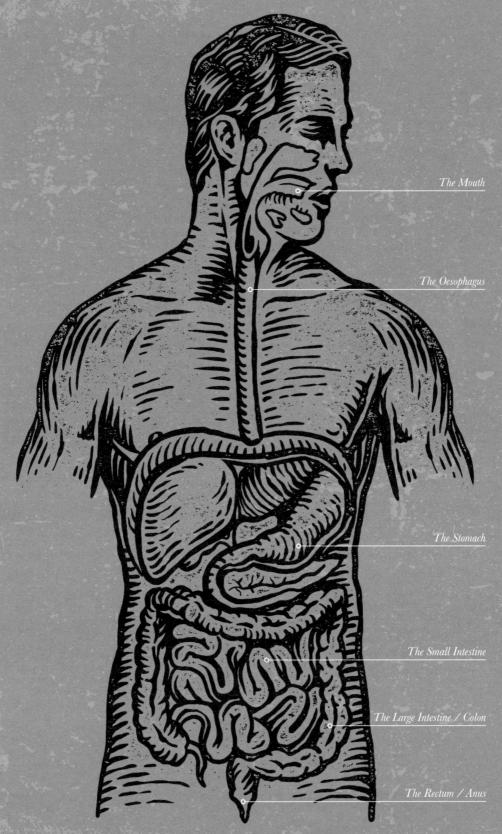

The Mouth

The Oesophagus

The Stomach

The Small Intestine

The Large Intestine / Colon

The Rectum / Anus

DIGESTION

——

Whether it's carbohydrates, proteins or fats, once we ingest food, the goal of digestion is to break those long chain compounds into their component parts: carbohydrates into simple sugars, proteins into amino acids and fats into fatty acids. Once those building blocks are released, they pass into the blood, to the liver and are then ordered and reassembled wherever our body needs them. That could be amino acids being assembled into proteins for muscle growth, simple sugars joined and stored for energy as glycogen or, if we've overdone it a bit, fatty acids stored as adipose tissue. Our bodies are basically chemical factories, constantly breaking down and reassembling materials. The important thing to remember, as a plant-based cyclist, is that as long as you supply your factory with all the basic raw materials it needs, it doesn't matter whether those materials come from plant or animal sources.

The Mouth

Digestive health and function starts in the mouth. We take in the food and, by the mechanical process of chewing, form a bolus of food that can then be swallowed. During this first stage, enzymes – such as salivary amylase and lipase, breaking down carbohydrates and fats respectively – are also introduced which begin the chemical breakdown of the food. Saliva is an important part of the immune system, producing antibodies such as IgA and anti-microbial compounds. It also provides lubrication for the bolus of food meaning, if you're not properly hydrated and have

a dry mouth, your digestion will suffer. Your granny was right when she nagged at you to chew your food as, if you don't chew for long enough, this first vital stage of digestion is compromised. If you tend to rush your food, taking time to chew properly could make a big difference to your digestion and gut health. Both hydration and chewing are among the reasons why vegetable juices are so effective for helping riders maintain gut health during Grand Tours. The juice keeps them well hydrated and, at the end of a big day, when they're literally too tired to chew, it's a great way of getting nutrients into them.

The Stomach

Once swallowed, the food travels down your oesophagus via rhythmic contraction and relaxation of muscles known as peristalsis. It then enters the stomach via a one-way sphincter valve. The valve prevents the acidic content of the stomach from back flowing, damaging the unprotected lining of the oesophagus and causing the unpleasant sensation of heartburn.

The stomach is essentially a big churning muscular sack full of acid that breaks food down mechanically and chemically. The extremely harsh acidic environment also helps to kill off any harmful microbes that may be in the food. It is distensible and can normally expand to hold about one litre of food. After an hour or two in the stomach, a thick semi-liquid called chyme is produced.

The Small Intestine

This chyme is slowly released into your small intestine where the majority of digestion and absorption occurs and, when I talk about gut health, this is the area that's really important to focus on. As the chyme leaves the stomach, pancreatic juices are secreted into it from the gall bladder, breaking down the nutrients into their constituent building blocks ready for absorption and, as it's alkaline, it also neutralises the highly acidic stomach contents. This is vital as, for the small intestine to function optimally, it has to have an alkaline environment and we'll discuss this later in the chapter.

The small intestine, like the rest of the digestive tract, is effectively outside of the body. This can be a hard idea to grasp but the whole of our digestive system is a long tube that goes through our body and protects our insides from what's in it. If you injected partially digested food straight into the bloodstream or somehow got it into the body cavity, the results would be catastrophic. We have two openings at either end of the tube, the mouth and the anus, but there are no direct openings into the body. So any nutrients our cells and body need have to get from the 'outside' of the digestive tract, across the barrier lining of the gut and into our bloodstream. To enable this to occur the small intestine is lined with millions of one-cell-thick finger-like projections called microvilli, which massively increase the surface area and, therefore, facilitate the absorption of nutrients. A healthy small intestine is also densely populated by good bacteria, also known as microbiota (microbioam) or gut fauna, which aid the digestive process and helps to support the immune system.

The Large Intestine / Colon

Some further absorption of nutrients takes place here but this area of the gut is primarily concerned with the uptake of water, drawing it out of the passing mass of largely indigestible food matter. The large intestine is also a very important part of the immune system, with its good bacteria playing a key role. Fibre plays a really important role in the large intestine and colon, helping to form the bulk of stool, keeping it soft.

The Rectum / Anus

Waste material from the digestive process constitutes the faecal mass, which is stored in the rectum prior to excretion via the anus. If your digestive system is healthy, you should be having at least two bowel movements per day, if not you may not be getting enough fibre.

DIGESTION

"You should have at least two bowel movements per day"

- ARE WE COWS OR CATS? -

When discussing our diet, especially when considering plant-based diets, it's interesting to see how our digestive anatomy compares to other species and how that might indicate the type of diet we're adapted to.

At one end of the dietary scale you have cats, which are obligate carnivores. This means they can only digest meat. As you can see from the illustration below, they have an extremely short digestive tract, evolved for the fast digestion of meat protein and totally unsuited to the digestion of any plant or vegetable matter.

At the other end are the ruminants, cows and goats, which have evolved an extremely complicated system of stomach compartments. By fermenting their food through microbial action and bringing it back up into the mouth to chew a second time, they're able to extract nutrients from cellulose plant matter.

So, looking at our digestive tract, it's neither the short pure meat eater's nor the complex ruminant's, but somewhere in the middle. Although our vestigial appendix does suggest a plant eating ancestor, we've evolved as true omnivores – also indicated by our teeth and jaw – and, with a 'hybrid' digestive system, we're able to thrive on a variety of diets. From a food and nutrition point of view this makes us the ultimate survivor and capable of adapting to and thriving on a wide variety of foods and diets.

DIGESTION

GUT PROBLEMS & SOLUTIONS

———

We are gaining a better understanding of gut health; there is increasing research showing that the importance of the microbiome can be thought of as an ecological environment containing microorganisms. Some of these help and support health and some can be a health challenge for the host human. This microbiome can be affected by many conditions, and we need to be careful to maintain a healthy gut 'microbiota'.

Cyclists are particularly vulnerable to gut issues: these are multifactorial but one of the conditions that seem to affect the cyclists' gut is excess acidity caused by the excessive consumption of acid forming and acidic foods. If these foods are consumed, the buffering capabilities of pancreatic juices are challenged, resulting in an acidic and unhealthy gut environment. Modern diets, heavy in animal protein and processed food, tend to be very acid forming and are probably one of the main causes of the multitude of digestive ailments that are now prevalent and sadly often seen as normal and unavoidable. The clue is in the name of the building blocks of proteins, amino acids. They're acids and if your diet is very protein heavy, your gut will be too. Fortunately predominately plant-based diets tend to be far more carbohydrate heavy and therefore

> "The small intestine is an incredibly sensitive environment"

alkaline forming, resulting in generally better gut health. Anecdotally, when I followed a plant-based diet, indigestion, which I had suffered from in the past, stopped completely. Also when I speak to non-meat eaters they tend to have fewer stomach problems. This may be because the plant-based diet tends to be higher in fibre, and adherents generally pay more attention to the quality of their diet and nutrition.

As we've seen from the effect of excess acidity, the small intestine is an incredibly sensitive environment and the integrity and effectiveness of the villi is easily compromised. Research has shown that even drinking acidic water can affect the microbiome and when tested on mice this can even lead to an increase in type 1 diabetes. If this occurs it can have a number of negative effects. It can reduce the amount of nutrients extracted from the food, cause sensations of discomfort and bloating and some of the undigested food matter, bacteria and toxins can pass directly through it into the bloodstream, so called 'leaky gut syndrome'.

Each individual villi is separated from its neighbour by a tight protein barrier. If the villi are damaged or 'stressed', these protein barriers can break down and gaps can appear. These gaps then allow the transport of unwanted chemicals from the gut lumen into

THE PLANT-BASED CYCLIST

the 'body'. These chemicals include toxins that normally would not pass the gut barrier. There are now a few tests that can help identify if this is a problem with an individual. Many of these tests are pretty simple and rely on the assumption that compounds added to a drink are not normally absorbed through the gut, therefore if they are present in the urine of someone who has taken the drink this would suggest that there are issues with the individual's gut permeability. I like to use these tests with athletes when we are trying to understand the gut issues of the athlete. It can also act as an objective marker to see if particular interventions are having an effect.

Acidity/alkalinity is measured by pH, which refers to the concentration of hydrogen ions and is represented on a scale of zero-14. Below seven is acidic, seven is neutral and above seven is alkaline. I am not advocating that people should avoid all acidic foods but instead to be more aware of the foods they eat and the possible impact on gut health of acid forming foods.

In the column on the right is a list of foods which are mainly acidic or alkaline. It may help people understand why they may get more reflux from having coffee or chocolate or other acidic foods. One interesting anomaly is lemon juice. In the pure state of juice it is an acid but when digested and metabolised it becomes alkaline.

If people are really interested in this area it may be worth buying one of the many alkalising diet books. I have included black tea in the more acid-forming list; this is not because it is super acidic but because it is more acidic than green tea. This is because when the green tea is oxidised to form black tea this changes the pH of the tea.

Examples Of Acid & Alkali Forming Foods

MORE ACID FORMING

MEAT

DAIRY

COFFEE

SOFT DRINKS SUCH AS COLA

CHOCOLATE

MOST SPORTS DRINKS

WHITE BREAD

BLACK TEA

MORE ALKALI FORMING

NUTS

GREEN LEAFY VEGETABLES

GREEN TEA

TOFU

SOYA MILK

SWEET POTATO

RICE

WHOLEMEAL BREAD AND RYE BREAD ARE LESS ACIDIC

VEGETABLE JUICE

GUT PROBLEMS & SOLUTIONS

Along with sports drinks and diets often heavy in protein, cyclists are also subjected to a lot of other stressors that can affect gut vulnerability and function. When riding hard, blood is diverted away from servicing the digestive system to your working muscles. Riding in hot conditions and associated rises in core temperature can have a negative effect. Road spray getting onto bottles and then being ingested is one of the biggest causes of gut issues for riders and again, can lead to longer lasting issues with gut integrity. A good pro tip to prevent this in wet or muddy conditions is to spray a bit of fluid away before drinking to clear the nozzle. So, with this much going on, it's really important to do everything you can to help your gut cope with the load that your riding is putting on it.

> "Road spray on bottles being ingested is a big cause of gut issues"

For many riders the symptoms of a sub-optimally functioning gut are fairly mild and are often just accepted as normal or casually written off by expressions such as 'gel guts'. However, any sensations of bloating, sluggishness, excessive wind or acid reflux are often signs of an issue and can often fairly easily be addressed and cured. Don't forget, if your

- SPORTS DRINKS -

Many sports drinks are extremely acidic and, if you're consuming a lot of these when on the bike, this can have a negative effect on your gut health. The solution is to use a pH neutral sports drink. In the early 2000s when I was working with British Cycling, a lot of the mountain bikers were having stomach issues. I put my mind to this and determined two contributing factors. The first was the sheer intensity of the racing, which put a big strain on their digestion but the second was the amount of sports drink they were consuming. I measured the pH of the mix they were using and found it was 3.5, which is really acidic but not uncommon. Working with the University of Portsmouth we devised a study comparing the effect on using a normal versus a pH neutral sports drink on gastric distress. We found that using the pH neutral sports drink almost completely eradicated the gut issues that riders were getting. From that day I've always insisted that riders use pH neutral sports drinks. There are now commercially available sports drink mixes that are pH neutral so you should definitely try to use one.

*pH neutral energy drinks
can help solve gut issues*

gut isn't functioning properly, you won't be utilising your food effectively and this is likely to be affecting your performance. In more severe cases, the lethargy can affect training, race preparation and the severe bloating and cramping can be extremely debilitating.

I've seen this numerous times with athletes across a lot of sports and almost always a few dietary interventions have led to massive improvements. I remember the case of a professional rider who came to a team I was working with and claimed that he had gluten intolerance. This was without any medical diagnosis or testing and, when he described how it tended to flare up during the second and third week of a Grand Tour, I suspected it was a 'temporary gluten intolerance' caused by a stressed and a poorly functioning gut. I've seen this a number of times, especially

regarding gluten and lactose, where the perceived 'intolerance' is a sign of the gut being under stress. With the super gut friendly dietary protocol I had the riders on, his 'gluten intolerance' cleared up. I asked him towards the end of his first Tour de France how his gluten intolerance was and he said it'd completely gone and he could eat whatever he wanted.

*Rice cakes (recipe on p231)
are great to aid a gut rehab*

WORLD TOUR PLANT-BASED GUT REHAB PLAN

——

The plan below is aimed to help riders recover from a gut disturbance or for riders with a known sensitive gut to be used proactively before going into times of high physical stress. This could include travelling or a planned hard training or racing block.

This Gut Rehab Plan should be followed for three-five days to give your gut a rest while still providing all the nutrients you require. You should notice benefits within 24 hours and, when you've been symptom free for three days, you can start reintroducing the foods you've been avoiding.

Take a probiotic with each meal. This doesn't have to be a supplement; you can make your own kombucha tea (see the recipe on p144).

Avoid wheat and gluten, as gluten can be an extra irritant on the small intestine even if you're not allergic or intolerant.

Dairy-eating vegetarians should also avoid lactose. Like gluten, people who have gastric issues often have a mild temporary lactose intolerance. You can eat up to 100g of natural yoghurt a day as the manufacturing process breaks down much of the lactose.

AVOID HARD-TO-DIGEST GLUTEN	REPLACE WITH EASIER-TO-DIGEST GLUTEN
BREAD *PASTA* *BISCUITS*	*PORRIDGE OATS* *RICE* *POTATOES* *QUINOA*

AVOID HARD-TO-DIGEST DAIRY	REPLACE WITH EASIER-TO-DIGEST DAIRY
COW'S MILK *CHEESE* *BUTTER*	*SOYA MILK* *RICE MILK* *ALMOND MILK*

AVOID HARD-TO-DIGEST PROTEIN	REPLACE WITH EASIER-TO-DIGEST PROTEIN
NUTS *BEANS*	*LENTILS* *TOFU* *VEGAN QUORN*

OTHER IRRITANTS TO AVOID	
COFFEE *TEA (FRUIT TEA IS FINE)* *HIGH SUGAR FOODS*	*FRUIT JUICES (BECAUSE OF THE HIGH FERMENTABLE SUGAR CONTENT)* *ALCOHOL*

FRIENDLY BACTERIA

—

As we already mentioned, good bacteria densely populate a healthy intestine. These good bacteria are often referred to as probiotics. The food that these bacteria consume in your gut is plant derived fibre and is known as prebiotics. It is important that we carefully define probiotics. The World Health Organisation (WHO) define probiotics as: "Live microorganisms which when administered in adequate amounts confer a health benefit on the host; in order to be labelled a probiotic, scientific evidence for the health benefit would have to be documented". There are a lot of products on the market that are labelled as probiotics but actually do not satisfy this definition.

Obviously, if you're eating a plant-based diet, it's likely that you'll be providing your friendly bacteria with plenty of food! I personally do not believe that most people need to take probiotic supplements to maintain a diverse gut fauna and have a healthy gut. However with professional cyclists I do tend to use a supplement that combines probiotics and prebiotics as part of a safety net strategy. You have to remember the stress that their bodies are under with their volume and intensity of racing, training and amount of travel; even the hardest working amateurs are nowhere near that level. However if you are under a lot of stress – both physical or mental – or travelling, a short course of probiotic supplements certainly won't hurt.

The important thing though is to ensure that you're obtaining a wide range of probiotics. What we're really starting to understand is not just the vital role these good bacteria play in your gut but for your body and health as a whole. They're vital for a robust immune system and studies have shown a correlation between probiotic density and diversity and a lower incidence of chest infections. The way they're thought to do this is by protecting the integrity of the microvilli, preventing gut leakage and, by doing so, lowering systemic stress on the body.

However, not all bacteria are good. If gut conditions aren't optimal, conditions can occur which are more conducive to the proliferation of bad bacteria. These bacteria ferment the fibre, producing toxins, gas and reducing villi function.

Naturally fermented foods are a great way to ensure that a diverse range of bacteria is entering your gut and you should try to include these regularly in your diet. It's no coincidence that almost every population in the world has developed its own fermented food as, along with being a natural way to preserve the shelf life and store foods, we've always been aware of their health benefits.

> "Ensure that a diverse range of bacteria is entering your gut"

However, with refrigeration, freezing and artificial preservatives, we moved away from these amazing foods but thankfully we know

EF Education's Mitch Docker makes his own kombucha tea

seem to be rediscovering them. However these fermented foods such as Kefir and kombucha tea do not fall into the WHO definition of probiotics but are fermented foods. This does not mean that people do not find them useful, but the science is not there to be able to make the claim of being a probiotic.

Mitch Docker, one of the peloton's strongmen, makes his own kombucha tea and brings it to races with him. This is a fermented beverage based on tea and is really easy to make, it tastes refreshing and, when I have tried it, I have felt an almost immediate effect on how good my stomach feels. This may be psychological but I liked it. I have started making it myself now (see the simple recipe for it on p144). However, it is becoming more available ready-made, so check out the chiller section in your supermarket.

Fermented Foods To Add To Your Diet:

- Kombucha tea
- Pickles, such as gherkins
- Live dairy-free yogurts, such as coconut or soya
- Miso
- Sauerkraut (pickled cabbage)
- Japanese pickled horseradish
- Kimchi (Korean salted and fermented vegetables)

- SUMMARY -
MAINTAINING A HEALTHY DIGESTIVE SYSTEM

Cope With The Stress

Even under the duress of severe illness or a Grand Tour by taking care of your gut you'll be able to ensure that you get the most out of the food you consume. If you fail to address any gut health or digestive issues, no matter how optimal your diet, you'll never perform to your potential.

A Production Line

During digestion we mechanically and chemically break our food down into its constituent components: proteins into amino acids, fats into fatty acids, carbohydrates into simple sugars and all of the micronutrients. These are then absorbed into the bloodstream, dispatched around the body and reassembled where needed. As long as all of the building blocks are made available, it doesn't matter if they come from plant or animal sources.

Adaptable

Our anatomy points to us being one of evolution's ultimate omnivores, with a digestive system that's capable of extracting nutrients from a wide range of food sources. This makes us incredibly adaptable and is a strong reason for having confidence that you can survive, thrive and perform on a plant-based diet.

Don't Just Accept It

Whether it's an intolerance of a certain food type, regular wind or bloating or nausea after or during a hard ride, don't just accept digestive issues as being the norm. In a huge number of cases, by taking some simple steps and paying closer attention to gut health, such issues can often be completely and permanently resolved.

Ferment & Juice

Two tasty and simple ways to improve your gut health are to include more fermented foods and vegetable juice in your diet. The first will introduce a wide range of friendly bacteria into your gut and the second will produce a more alkaline environment for them to thrive in. Additionally, you'll be upping your intake of micronutrients without adding bulk to your diet. Win, win, and win.

*Top: Long rides or races can leave
many suffering from a bad gut...*

*Right: ...but don't accept it! It can
be remedied and avoided altogether*

05

MAINTAINING
A HEALTHY
DIGESTIVE SYSTEM

—

RECIPES

Knowledge

Recipes

——

**The essential know-how and
recipes to help banish 'gel guts'!**

Vegan & Vegetarian Friendly

KOMBUCHA TEA

—

Ingredients
20 portions

4 litres of water (if using tap water this should be boiled for 10 minutes and cooled to kill off any bacteria present and reduce chlorine)
4-6 tea bags or 4-6 teaspoons loose leaf tea
1 cup (200g) sugar
Kombucha Mother Culture: SCOBY
1-2 cups (250-500ml) strong starter liquid, aka well-fermented kombucha (usually included when buying a SCOBY)

Equipment

Pot or tea kettle for boiling water
Brewing vessel (at least four litres)
Stirring spoon
Muslin cloth and rubber band
Bottles with tightly closing lids

For successful kombucha tea you need a kombucha 'SCOBY', this is an acronym for Symbiotic Culture of Bacteria and Yeast. These can be purchased on the internet or if you know someone who makes their own they will probably be happy to give you some. A lot of recipes recommend purified or distilled water. This is mainly because of the high levels of chlorine and minerals in the water that can damage the SCOBY. If using tap water this can be minimised by boiling the water for 10 minutes in an open pan to allow the chlorine to evaporate. Water filters can also be used.

Method
Boil one litre of water. Add hot water and tea bags to pot or brewing vessel, steep for 10-15 minuets then remove the tea bags. Add sugar and stir to dissolve. Add the remaining three litres of water to the brewing vessel containing the sweetened 'tea'.

When the sweetened tea mix is at body temperature add the SCOBY and starter liquid. You should have about a 5cm space above the mixture and top of the brewing vessel to allow breathing space. Cover with cloth and secure in place with a rubber band.

Place the container in a warm, ventilated area out of direct sunlight for seven to 21 days (depends on taste). 75-85°F (24-29°C) is the best range, 80°F (27°C) is ideal. It may or may not get fizzy. The SCOBY may rise to the top or sink to the bottom, doesn't matter, the new culture will always form at the top.

After seven days, or when you are ready to taste your kombucha tea, gently insert a straw beneath the SCOBY and take a sip. If too tart, then reduce your brewing cycle next time. If too sweet, allow to brew for a few more days. Continue to taste every day or so until you reach your personal flavour preference. Your own kombucha recipe may vary.

Set aside your SCOBY(s) and starter liquid (two cups if possible) for the next batch from the top of the current brew. You may put them in any vessel. In order to make the kombucha fizzy you give it a second fermentation. Do this by decanting your kombucha into bottles and add a teaspoon of sugar into each. Seal with an airtight cap and place back in the warm place for about three days. Try the kombucha – it should be ready to drink and, to prevent further fermentation, keep in a cool place.

Nutritional Breakdown

MACRO STATS	PER 100g	PER 100g SERVING
CALORIES	20	20
CARBOHYDRATE	5g	5g
PROTEIN	0g	0g
FAT	0g	0g

Having a yoghurt to hand gives an easy lift to many dishes and snacks

- NUTRITION KNOWLEDGE -
DAIRY-FREE YOGHURT

There a lot of live dairy-free yogurts on the market today. They tend to have beneficial probiotic strains such a *S.thermophilus*, *L. bulgaricus*. Many of these commercially available products are also fortified with vitamins B12 and D2, however there's no reason why you can't make your own dairy-free yoghurts.

Yoghurt making is really easy: you can buy home yoghurt making kits, which regulate the environment to make it optimal for the yoghurt culture.

You can use pretty much any dairy-free milk but I find soya makes the best dairy-free yoghurt and it has the best protein profile (see table in Chapter 7, p175). You'll need to buy a starter culture but these are easily available.

You add the culture to the milk, place in the temperature-controlled kit and it takes about 24 hours for it to become yoghurt. Some people like to add a thickener to the yoghurt to make it more like a dairy yogurt but this is not essential.

Soluble fibre can easily become a big part of a plant-based diet

- NUTRITION KNOWLEDGE -
FIBRE

———

We've already mentioned fibre when looking at friendly bacteria but that's just one way in that it's important for gut health. There are two types of fibre: soluble and insoluble. Soluble fibre is found in foods such as oats, legumes and brown rice and effectively helps to lubricate your gut. Insoluble fibre is the indigestible cellulose plant matter, such as whole grain, and its main function is to form the bulk of the stool. So, the two types of fibre effectively work in tandem. The insoluble fibre providing something for the gut to push against and the soluble fibre helping it along its way.

If you're consuming a balanced largely plant-based diet, it's more than likely that you're consuming plenty of fibre. In fact, there are times when you might want to consciously dial back on your intake of insoluble fibre. High levels of insoluble fibre in your diet can lead to a significant and weighty amount of matter in your digestive tract and will leave you needing the loo more often. Neither of these situations is ideal for long, multiple day or mountainous events. So, in the lead up to and during events and training rides that meet these criteria, going lower in insoluble fibre can be a good idea.

With pro riders, in the lead up to key events, the go-to food is rice. It's easily digestible, low in insoluble fibre and a great source of energy. Even by switching to a lower fibre diet in the 24-48 hours before an event, this can reduce their bodyweight by up to kilogram, make them more comfortable holding an aggressive position on the bike and less likely to have to stop to go to the loo. On the bike they'll predominately eat rice cakes (see recipe in Chapter 8, p231), a great source of easily digestible energy, with a high fluid content and very low residue.

- NUTRITION KNOWLEDGE -

SUGGESTED PLANT-BASED LOW RESIDUE DIET MEAL OUTLINE

If you have an important event coming up, you might want to try a low residue diet. Experiment with using it before a few training rides and see how you feel on it. It's important though that you should only reduce fibre intake temporarily and occasionally. As mentioned, fibre provides a fuel for the microbioam so these plans should not be followed for more than several days.

To maintain soluble fibre intake you should include a glass of vegetable juice, prune juice or energised greens with each meal (see below). It can be challenging to get adequate protein with a plant-based low residue diet and you need to pay attention to this. The main low residue high protein plant-based foods are tofu, dairy-free milks/yoghurts (soya) and vegetable-based protein powders.

BREAKFAST	*Bowl of low fibre breakfast cereal e.g. Rice Crispies, using dairy-free milk* *Or white toast with honey, maple syrup or Marmite* *Or rice with tofu (150g)* *Glass of vegetable juice, energised greens or prune juice tea*
ON BIKE	*Rice cakes, energy drinks, gels*
LUNCH	*White rice or mashed potato, tofu (150g) or 20g of vegetable protein* *Glass of vegetable juice, energised greens or prune juice tea*
DINNER	*White rice or mashed potato, tofu (150g), vegetable juice* *Glass of vegetable juice, energised greens or prune juice tea*
SUPPER	*Dairy-free yoghurt (200ml plain) and honey or maple syrup*
SNACKS	*Only soft and easily digested fruit such as ripe bananas* *Carbohydrate-electrolyte sports drink, squashes and cordials* *Rice cakes, rice crackers*

Fermented Foods To Add To Your Diet:

- Drink plenty of water while following this programme, other drinks allowed include tea and coffee (as tolerated), herbal teas (strained), cordials/squashes and soda drinks
- Eliminate all fibre sources e.g. smooth juices, no fruit and no whole grains etc.
- Use only white bread, white rice, pasta, clear soups, stock or broths

Gels are great for when you
need a fast acting energy boost

Fresh vegetable and fruit juices are simple but incredibly effective

NUTRITION KNOWLEDGE

- NUTRITION KNOWLEDGE -
JUICING

—

During extended periods of hard training or on multiple day events, vegetable juice is brilliant. It provides riders with the nutrients they need, helps to alkalise the gut and feeds the gut friendly probiotics but without the excessive bulk of insoluble fibre. It's staggering how much vegetable juice pro riders will consume when you make it available to them – it's almost as though they sense the good it does them. As with many good things, the nutritional industry has productised vegetable juice with various 'super green' and 'energised greens' powders and drinks. These are usually just

> "Vegetable juice provides riders the nutrients they need"

highly concentrated and dried vegetables extracts and tend to taste pretty bad.

For this reason they'll then add flavourings and sweeteners, undoing some of the good of the product. You're far better making your own from fresh (see Chapter 7, p179 for advice and information on buying a juicer). The recipes on the opposite page are suggestions to get you started but feel free to experiment and use whatever you have to hand and in season.

Vegan & Vegetarian Friendly

JUICE RECIPES

—

Ingredients
2 portions each

Beetroot, carrot, celery, apple and ginger juice
2 small beetroot (approx. 100g)
3 carrots (approx. 200g)
2 sticks of celery (approx. 100g)
½ apple
A large 2cm thumb of ginger

Beetroot, cucumber, carrot and pineapple juice
2 small beetroot (approx. 100g)
½ large cucumber
3 carrots (approx. 200g)
½ pineapple, peeled

Beetroot, carrot, celery, apple and ginger juice
A real favourite with pro riders I've worked with. The sweetness of the apple helps to mask some of the vegetable taste of the other ingredients, which some people struggle with. The ginger adds a really interesting and warming note and has a number of supposed health benefits. Serves two (approximately).

Beetroot, cucumber, carrot and pineapple juice
Another tried and tested combination that'll particularly appeal if you have a sweet tooth. Serves two (approximately).

Method
For both of these recipes, simply wash and chop the ingredients and then follow your juicer's operating instructions. Drink as soon after preparing as possible or chill to consume within 24 hours. The ingredients will separate and settle so you will need to stir/shake the juice before juicing. You can also freeze: use an ice cube tray to make vegetable juice cubes to add to smoothies.

MONITORING YOUR DIET & HEALTH

—

Knowing your body's condition is
invaluable for health and performance.

- CHAPTER 6 -

MONITORING YOUR DIET & HEALTH

—

As we've seen in previous chapters, as long as your diet is varied, balanced and you pay attention to a few specific concerns, there's no reason why a plant-based diet can't support optimum health and performance.

In fact, there are plenty of reported health benefits to a plant-based diet and, from my own experience of following one, I certainly felt well, and I found that my exercise performance improved.

> "There are plenty of health benefits to a plant-based diet"

However, this is not always the case. A friend of mine, who was a keen cyclo-cross racer, made the change to a plant-based diet during the race season. He welcomed the initial weight loss he achieved but, despite thinking that he was eating enough and eating healthily, the kilos kept dropping off, along with his form and energy levels. A bit of digging and comparing his meat eating and plant-based diets found that his overall calorie and protein consumption had dropped significantly. He'd basically just removed the meat and dairy from his diet and not replaced the macronutrients and calories they were supplying. A few simple tweaks, such as using vegan protein shakes, stirring some coconut oil into his morning porridge and a more planned, organised and structured approach to his daily diet overall, soon had him maintaining a stable weight and able to train and race at and above his meat eating level. The weight he had lost was mainly muscle and a relatively small amount of fat as his body tried to cope with the significantly reduced caloric intake. This can be a common issue with people making the switch to a plant-based diet or reducing their intake of animal-based foods. This can be compounded, as, with endurance sports, weight loss is often perceived to always be a good thing. If he'd carried on in this way, in the longer term he would have also developed problems around micronutrients as discussed in Chapter Four (starts on p102).

If you race or train hard, it can pay to get regular check-ups

By monitoring a few areas, he could have easily prevented his performance and wellbeing crash and made his transition to a plant-based diet far less painful. This doesn't just apply to athletes following or transitioning to a plant-based diet though. Anyone who is training, racing and, in doing so, putting high demands on their body, owes it to themself to take a proactive approach to their health. Unfortunately, for the majority of amateur cyclists, their approach tends to be more reactive and they'll only seek advice and guidance when something goes wrong.

They can definitely learn from the pros and, by investing some time and probably a bit of money in monitoring their health, could avoid many potential blips and lay-offs due to illness and injury.

> "Investing time in monitoring health could avoid lay-offs"

Eating high protein foods during weight loss protects lean mass

ENERGY BALANCE

—

Energy balance refers to the total energy coming into our bodies as food versus the energy we expend. If your energy balance is positive, you're consuming more calories than you're using and you'll gain weight. Conversely, if you're expending more than you're consuming, you'll lose weight. Up to a certain point, a slightly negative energy balance, approximately 500kcals per day, will result in steady fat loss. However, if that negative energy balance is maintained for a long period of time and your fat reserves get too low or are excessive, your body's evolved starvation response will cause it to hold onto fat and to plunder its own muscle tissue for energy. As far as your body is concerned, you're still eking out a marginal existence on the savannah; the low calorie intake means a famine and your body is doing what it can to keep you alive. It doesn't know if you're purposely cutting those calories in an attempt to improve your climbing performance, or even for a beach holiday!

However, as we have seen from our example of the cyclo-cross racer at the start of this chapter, simply cutting out animal products – without considering how to replace those calories and macronutrients – can result in a significant calorie deficit. This could easily equate to 1000-3000kcals a day, which could have serious implications for health and performance. Additionally, during periods of intended weight loss, optimal protein intake is one of the primary strategies for maintaining lean tissue mass. If you have the double hit of an overly negative energy balance and sub-optimal protein intake – which can easily occur with a poor plant-based diet and a heavy training load – there are bound to be issues. A long-term excessive calorie deficit can lead to a condition known as 'relative energy deficiency in sport' or RED-S.

RED-S is the result of insufficient caloric intake and/or excessive energy expenditure. Consequences of this low-energy condition can alter many physiological systems, including metabolism, menstrual function, bone health, immunity, protein synthesis, and cardiovascular and psychological health. The RED-S concept has been adapted from a previously identified syndrome, the female athlete triad, which affects active women with low energy availability, menstrual dysfunction and low bone mineral density. Emerging data suggests there may be a parallel syndrome in undernourished male athletes with similar negative health consequences. One of the primary results of the condition in male athletes is a reduced testosterone level. Lower testosterone is fairly common among endurance athletes and one of the main indicators is a reduced libido. Of particular concern to both male and female cyclists is the reduction in bone density associated with RED-S as, with cycling being a non-weight bearing activity, this can be an issue anyway and will be further compounded.

> "Long-term excessive calorie deficit can lead to RED-S"

MONITORING YOUR ENERGY BALANCE

—

You'd think that monitoring your
energy balance would be a simple case
of logging your calories in and calories
out. Unfortunately, to do this accurately
is surprisingly difficult without access to
specialised laboratory equipment. The
first figure that contributes to your caloric
expenditure is your Basal Metabolic Rate
(BMR) and this is simply the energy your body
needs to exist. On top of this is the energy
required for you to go about your day-to-day
life, working, looking after the kids or doing
some DIY. Finally, as cyclists, you have the
energy required to fuel your training. There
are numerous calculators and online apps
that supposedly allow you to work out your
total energy requirement but at best they're
a rough estimate. Even when it comes to
totalling up the energy you've expended in
training, they often forget one crucial factor.
As you become fitter, you become more
efficient and use less energy and very few
models take this into account.

Be very sceptical of estimates of the calories
burned from exercise. Apps and tracking
programs that just use simple metrics, such
as your height, weight, time and distance, are
typically between 20-60% out. Using a heart
rate monitor will improve the estimate to
within 10-20% accuracy. With a well-calibrated
power meter, you're probably looking at
within 5%. So, on a four hour ride that might
burn 2500kcals – even with a power meter –
the figure you'd get would be 125kcals over
or under; using a heart rate monitor that rises

to be up to 500kcals out. Given that the daily
deficit for safe weight loss is 500kcals, you
can see the problem.

On the other side of the equation, although
there are a number of apps and other
resources for keeping food diaries and
logging your calorie intake, it's incredibly
easy – whether through the data on the
app, which is often user supplied, or during
your food preparation and logging – for
errors to creep in. Although such apps can
be useful for providing a rough indication
of caloric and macronutrient intake – just
like BMR calculators and caloric burn from
exercise data – don't rely on them. That said,
using such methods is a reasonable starting
point for getting a ballpark figure of your
expenditure and intake.

From that starting point you should adopt a
monitoring approach of the impact of your
diet on your body and then, based on this,
adjust it accordingly. This is the approach I
take with the pro riders and other athletes
under my care. I'll monitor body composition,
weight, training load and diet and see how
they affect one another in any individual rider.
Once a data trend starts appearing I can then
tweak the rider's intake to achieve the goals
we want. This may take a bit more time but
in the long term is far more effective than just
attempting to track calories.

*Monitor the impact on your
body rather than count calories*

*Adam Hansen is vegan and has
completed 20 consecutive Grand Tours*

BODY COMPOSITION

———

Monitoring changes in body composition, rather than weight alone, is probably the best way to check if you're consuming enough calories.

The most convenient option for doing this at home is bioimpedance scales. These work by you standing on two plates (and sometimes also holding handles) that pass a small undetectable electric current through your body. Various body tissue types, due to the amount of water in them, conduct the current differently and so, the relative amounts can be deduced. Although the actual body fat percentage given should be taken with a pinch of salt, as long as measurements are taken at the same time of day and in a similar hydration state, for establishing and monitoring personal trends they're perfectly adequate. I'd recommend first thing in the morning after you've been to the loo.

If you find that your weight is dropping but this isn't accompanied by a proportionate drop in the reported body fat percentage, you should suspect that you're losing lean tissue and are under-fuelling and/or not having enough protein.

My personal choice for tracking a rider's body composition are skin fold measurements taken at eight sites around the body. There are equations and tables that allow you to convert the skin folds total to a percentage figure but I prefer to stick to and work from a sum of the skin folds. The percentage figure, calculated using regression equations, will always only be an estimate. One formula or table might give an athlete 10% body fat but, using a different one, they'll come out at 15%. By just using the sum of the sites and measuring at regular intervals of four to eight weeks, I can track an athlete's progress.

Most qualified personal trainers at your local gym should be able to perform an eight site skin fold assessment but it's vital that the measurements are consistent and are performed by the same individual each time. Remember though that it's the skin folds total that you're interested in, not the percentage figure from them.

There are more high tech solutions for monitoring body composition such as 'Body Pods' and DEXA (dual-energy X-ray absorptiometry) scans but, aside from possible interest value, what they offer beyond the methods previously described doesn't really justify their significantly higher cost.

Don't ignore lower tech or more subjective ways of monitoring body composition. Simple measurements using a tape measure can be very useful. How your clothing fits, especially unforgiving cycling kit can provide great insights into changes in body shape and composition. Shorts or a skinsuit becoming baggier around your thighs can be indicative of lean tissue loss. Finally, a simple 'nearly nude' photo taken in a full-length mirror can provide a great point of comparison.

No matter what your discipline, monitor a variety of metrics

PERFORMANCE, RECOVERY & GENERAL WELLBEING

PERFORMANCE, RECOVERY & GENERAL WELLBEING

Another indicator that there might be an issue with your diet is reduced performance or noticeably poorer or incomplete recovery. Again, the cyclo-cross racer we mentioned at the start of the chapter noticed his racing and training performance dropping and eventually had to stop racing completely.

There are now a number of excellent online training platforms that allow you to analyse training sessions and track changes in key metrics. Some of these – along with taking data from your bike computer – can also sync with bioimpedance scales and other health tracking gadgets. They also allow you to input and track metrics, such as sleep quality, motivation and mood, which can also provide invaluable indicators.

It should be noted that changes in performance could be fairly subtle and related to the nature of events and training you're doing. If you're mainly focused on sub-threshold endurance goals, you might not notice early warning signs of performance drop-off. However, for higher intensity performance, the results of losses in lean tissue will be far more obvious. This is one of the reasons why endurance athletes need to monitor a range of metrics to establish the effect of their training and diets on their bodies. Along with regular Functional Threshold Power (FTP) testing, you should also look for changes at the sharper end of your Power Curve, such as five-second power, even if this might not be a priority for your cycling.

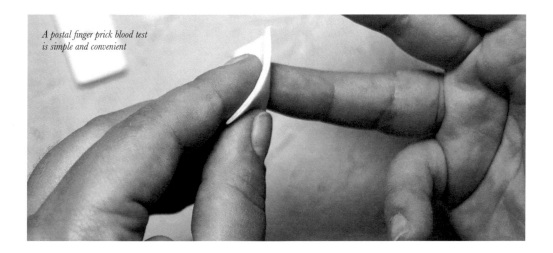

A postal finger prick blood test is simple and convenient

BLOOD SCREENING

——

For athletes, and even the general population in Europe, regular blood tests are an accepted part of life. You can just walk into a clinic, ask for a test, pay a few euros and get your results. However, in the UK, we only tend to have our blood values looked at when something has gone wrong and probably after a referral from a General Practitioner (a Primary Care Physician).

I encourage all of my athletes to have regular blood screenings as, by adopting a proactive approach, issues can be identified and remedied before the manifestation of negative physical symptoms.

There are now a number of companies who offer online blood screening for athletes. You're sent a kit, perform a simple finger prick test, pop the sample in the post and you'll receive e-mail notification when your results are available for you to view.

Key markers, including vitamin B12, vitamin D, ferritin (see Chapter Four, starts on p102) and hormonal profiles, are measured. Most providers produce an in-depth report to explain your results and some offer consultations with health professionals to make recommendations for any necessary interventions.

It's important that screenings are not viewed as a one off but should be performed every eight to 16 weeks. This allows your personal profile and baseline values to be determined as it's the changes and trends that are equally and arguably more important than the absolute values. The results are all based on a range and just because your results are on the low side that does not mean a deficiency, as this could be normal for you. It is more important to see the trends on how the levels go over time. For this reason, most of the companies offering these services work on a subscription basis.

- SUMMARY -
MONITORING YOUR DIET & HEALTH

——

A Poor Diet Is A Poor Diet

Simply changing to a plant-based diet does not necessarily make it healthy or suitable for supporting hard racing and training. Key macro and micronutrients, along with the calories, that animal products may have been providing, have to be replaced with plant-based sources.

Energy Balance

Energy balance refers to the total energy coming into our bodies as food versus the energy we expend. A chronic negative energy balance can lead to a serious condition known as RED-S. Although there are methods for tracking caloric intake and expenditure, they're fraught with inaccuracies and should be used as a rough starting point.

Body Composition

Body composition provides a tangible physical indication of the effect of your energy balance. By monitoring it, you can check whether your diet is providing the calories and macronutrients your body requires and adapt it accordingly. Bioimpedance scales can provide a quick and convenient method for monitoring body composition.

Performance & Wellbeing

Along with body composition, there's a wide range of performance and wellbeing metrics that you can track and monitor. From obvious drop offs in power data to more subtle changes, such as sleep quality and mood all can be indicative of issues with your diet.

Blood Screening

For any athlete, regular blood screening should be seen as a priority, rather than a luxury. This particularly applies if you're making significant changes to your diet, such as reducing or completely cutting out animal food sources. Online DIY testing services make blood screening convenient, easy and affordable.

All Of The Above

The more metrics you can monitor and track to gauge the impact of your diet on your health and performance, the better. By doing this, you'll be able to pick up and address potential issues before they begin to have a negative impact.

Top: You could also consider performance focused tests, like VO$_2$ max...

Right: ...or 'full-frontal' FTP tests, repeated at intervals to track fitness

THE PLANT-BASED KITCHEN

—

The equipment and store cupboard
essentials to set you up for success!

- CHAPTER 7 -

THE PLANT-BASED KITCHEN

When I followed a plant-based diet, I found that adopting a very organised and prepared approach to my meals was essential. Key to this was having a properly equipped kitchen, a well-stocked store cupboard, a good bank of reliable recipes and a proactive and thoughtful approach to travel. Obviously this applies to all diets but, although plant-based diets have become far more accepted and accommodated for in recent years, you can still find yourself marooned with little or, on occasions, no choice. If you're trying to optimally fuel training and racing, not having the nutrients you require when you need them is far from ideal.

Also, unless you are well organised, you can often find yourself resorting to the same go-to meal or reaching for pre-prepared convenience foods. As we've already discussed repeatedly, eating a wide range of plant-based food sources is key to obtaining all of the macro and micronutrients you require and, just because a ready meal is plant-based, that doesn't mean it won't be loaded with unnecessary salt, sugar, additives or preservatives. In this chapter, I'll go through the essentials to always have in your store cupboard, the kitchen equipment and gadgets that'll make your plant-based diet easier and some tips for travelling.

$\longrightarrow$

*Organisation and preparation are
the keys to plant-based success*

STORE CUPBOARD ESSENTIALS

——

The following list is by no means comprehensive but these are some of the basics that I'll always try to have in my cupboard. The question you should always be able to answer yes to is: "Could I make a decent meal from scratch right now?"

Cereals & Grains

Rice is an incredibly useful food for cyclists. Basmati rice especially is easy to digest and a great source of carbohydrates. Brown rice and wild rices will be higher in fibre and a number of micronutrients and, if you find them too heavy or filling on their own, can be mixed with basmati. You should also have some sticky rice for making rice cakes and dessert rice for pre-ride rice pudding.

Quinoa is one of the few complete plant-based protein sources and should be a staple. You can also get quinoa flakes that are great for making porridge with. Amaranth is a lesser-known pseudo-grain than quinoa but is also a complete protein source and can be used in much the same way. Buckwheat is another complete protein source and makes brilliant pancakes. Couscous, spelt, millet and bulgur are other carbohydrate options but aren't as protein-rich as the ones previously suggested.

No cyclist's store cupboard would be complete without oats for porridge and for making homemade energy bars.

Regular breakfast cereals are useful to have as they can provide a quick and easy snack option and are often fortified with a number of important micronutrients.

Although I haven't referred to it in the book specifically, having a few bags of egg-free pasta can be handy for putting together a quick and easy meal.

Nuts & Seeds

As we discussed with regards to protein and fats, a ride range of nuts and seeds is key to an optimal plant-based diet. A tub with a mixed nut selection provides a quick and easy high protein snacking option – just grab a handful. I'm especially a fan of pistachios as they have a great fat and protein profile.

Seeds, such as flax seeds, should be stored in their whole form and then ground as and when needed. Again, a tub with a selection of seeds will ensure you get a range of nutrients. A good mix would include: flax/linseed, sunflower, pumpkin, sesame and chia seeds.

Dried Fruit

Dedicate another big tub to a mix of dried fruit. Prunes and apricots are especially good and are great for adding to porridge, for using when making energy bars or for just snacking. Be a bit careful with the latter though as dried fruit is incredibly moreish, very energy dense and so it can be very easy to overdo it.

Beans, Peas & Pulses

You've guessed it, another big tub full of mixed beans. There's a massive range to choose from and the more variety you can get, the better. Varieties to look for include: borlotti, black eyed, black turtle, butter, haricot, lima, pinto, red kidney and mung. You can also add some split peas and chickpeas to this mix. Recently I have found high street supermarkets have started stocking bigger bags (one to two kilos) of mixed beans that will be better value. However, I still tend to buy the individual beans in bulk and then mix them myself.

There's always a bit of confusion as to whether you need to soak dried beans overnight. All soaking does is to reduce the final cooking time – it's the actual cooking that removes any toxins and makes the beans digestible. For many slow-cooked recipes, overnight soaking isn't necessary but it does certainly speed up cooking.

You'll also want to have a selection of lentils, both red and green. For efficiency I will often batch-cook lentils. I will portion out the cooked lentils and VacPac them using a food saver machine to use at a later date.

Oils

You can find loads of information on these in Chapter Two (starting on p48) and there's a massive variety for you to try and experiment with. However, I'll always have a decent olive oil, coconut oil, flax seed oil and –

more recently – I've also been using avocado oil more frequently.

Tins

Whether for making smoothies, curries, ice cream or even porridge, always have a few tins of coconut milk. I'll also always have some tinned tomatoes for knocking up a quick sauce for pasta or rice.

Tinned beans and lentils can be great when you want something really quick or, in the summer, want a salad and don't want to bother with lengthy cooking and cooling. Tins will always work out more expensive than their dried equivalents and you'll want to ensure you drain and rinse to remove the overly salty water they're often stored in, but having some in your larder as a standby is a good idea.

Similarly, you can get pouches of rice and other grains, such as quinoa, that are cooked and ready to eat or can just be heated in the microwave. These can also be good for travelling.

Herbs, Spices & Other Condiments

These come down to personal taste but the more flavours you can introduce into your meals, the greater the variety you're likely to consume. Nutritional yeast flakes are something I'd recommend everyone to have though. They're great for adding a slightly cheesy, nutty, savoury taste to dishes and can simply be sprinkled onto soups, salads and many other meals. They're often fortified with B12 and other important micronutrients too.

Plant-Based Protein Powder

I've mentioned plant-based protein powders throughout this book and, although it's possible to have an optimal plant-based diet without resorting to them,

Dried fruit adds a fuller energy punch to any bowl of porridge

they provide a convenient and easy fallback to ensure that your protein intake is sufficient. They've improved massively in terms of taste, ease of mixing and availability and are great to blitz into a smoothie, add to porridge, incorporate into pancake batter or just to have as a protein top-up before going to bed.

In The Fridge & Freezer
The freezer is a true ally of the busy plant-based cyclist. Every time you cook a meal, put a portion aside and freeze it. You'll soon have a stash of ready-to-go meals.

Also in the freezer, you can have a whole variety of frozen fruit and vegetables. Frozen fruit and vegetables can often have a better nutrient profile than their "fresh" equivalents. Frozen edamame beans (immature soybeans) should always be in your freezer.

Some blocks of tofu in the fridge always means that a tasty and nutritious stir-fry is only minutes away. Don't forget that tofu often requires draining and compressing before use.

Tofu is a fast go-to and easy
plant-based meal staple

Soy milk has the most similar
protein profile to cow's milk.

- NON-DAIRY MILKS -

Compared to a just a few years ago, there's now a whole range of non-dairy milks to choose from. As they're often fortified with essential micronutrients, such as B12, iron and calcium, they can play an important role in a healthy plant-based diet and, depending on the type, can also provide valuable protein.

The table below compares the nutritional value of a number of commonly available non-dairy milks to cow's milk. The information refers to a 240ml serving.

	PROTEIN	FAT	CARBOHYDRATES	CALORIES
COW'S MILK (WHOLE)	8g	8g	13g	146 kcals
SOY MILK	7-9g	4-4.5g	4g	80-90 kcals
ALMOND MILK	1g	2.5g	1-2g	30-35 kcals
COCONUT MILK	-	4g	-	45 kcals
OAT MILK	2.5 5g	4.5-5g	19-29g	140-170 kcals
RICE MILK	1g	2-3g	27-38g	130-140 kcals

As you can see from the table, if you're looking for a non-dairy milk that provides a similar amount of protein as cow's milk, then soy milk is your only real option.

STORE CUPBOARD ESSENTIALS

KITCHEN EQUIPMENT

—

Again, this isn't a mandatory or an absolute list, it's just the kit and gadgets that made my life easier when I was following a plant-based diet and devising the recipes for this book. I'll freely admit that I'm a bit of a gadget freak so you probably don't need them all!

KITCHEN EQUIPMENT

Rice Cooker

If I was limited to just one kitchen gadget, it'd be one of these and it's probably the first item that I ensure is on the team bus for cooking post-race recovery meals. They're not just for rice, you can cook any of the grains and pseudo-grains, such as quinoa, I've talked about in them; many also have a compartment for steaming vegetables in too.

Air Fryer

An air fryer allows you to get a frying effect but with a minimal amount of oil. I find them particularly good for cooking tofu as you can get a really good amount of crisping and texture, which is really difficult using traditional cooking methods. They're also good for roasted vegetables and because you're don't have to put a full oven on you're also saving energy. Like the Thermomix, many air fryers also have timers.

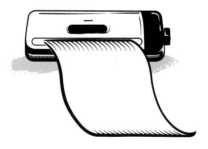

Food Vacuum Sealer

With these devices you place the food you want store in a sealed bag or special container and the vacuum sucks out the air and then seals the bag. They're great for using with mixed grains and lentils.

Thermomix

A Thermomix is essentially a multitude of kitchen gadgets in one. It grinds, chops, mixes, kneads, stirs, whisks, blends, steams, cooks, weighs and more. Buying one represents a big investment but I wouldn't be without mine. One of the real joys of the Thermomix is that you can put your ingredients in, put it on a timer, go out for a ride and come back to a delicious meal.

If your budget doesn't quite stretch to a Thermomix, you should get some accurate kitchen scales, a food processor and a cheap coffee grinder for milling seeds.

Slow Cooker Or Pressure Cooker

Both of these essentially do the same job; the slow cooker just does it slowly and the pressure cooker fast. For cooking pulses, a modern pressure cooker is hard to beat and, with many having a timer function, becomes really useful. I still love a traditional slow cooker and, for one of my favourite recipes, my five bean chilli (see p223), it's my go-to gadget. You can now get all-in-one multi-cookers that offer both slow and pressure cooking in one gadget and have a delayed timer. You can set your porridge to cook the night before so it's ready when you get up or have it cooking while you're out on your bike.

Kitchen gadgets aren't essential but they can make life easier

Juicer

Juicing has become really popular, we use it a lot with pro cycling and you can find some recipe suggestions in Chapter Five (starts on p124). I introduced juicing because during Grand Tours riders complained that eating all of the salads and vegetables would fill them up and, by the third week, they felt that the bulk was starting to ferment in their bowels. I thought the solution for this would be to provide juice for the riders, combining vegetables and fruit. This removes a lot of the insoluble fibre, which creates a lot of the bulk, however the soluble fibre – which maintains bowel function and feeds our good bacteria – is still in the juice. This became really popular and the chef would juice up to 10kg of vegetables and fruit each day!

There are two main types of domestic juicing machines: centrifuge and cold press (also known as masticating or triturating juicers).

A centrifuge machine spins the fruit and vegetables at high velocity and forces the juice through a fine mesh, thus separating the juice from the pulp. These tend to be faster and cheaper than the cold press, but I find they are not as effective for juicing soft fruit or leafy vegetables, such as spinach and kale. It

is also thought that the high speed spinning may generate heat that may denature some of the nutrients.

The cold press machines tend to be slower and, as the name suggests, these machines mash and press the fruit through a fine mesh, the separated pulp is usually in a pellet or small block. I find these are much more effective for soft fruit and leaves.

If you are going to juice you need to embrace it like a hobby because it can be a labor of love. When my children were at school they used to love me experimenting with different juices, they really like ones that contained beetroot and ginger. The worst one I made had asparagus as a key ingredient – I would not recommend that. The leftover pulp can be used in other recipes, such as cakes and bakes.

Knives

Even with the best gadgets, following a plant-based diet does involve chopping a fair bit of fruit and vegetables. Don't skimp when buying knives and make sure that you keep them sharp.

Cookware

Like knives, decent cookware makes all the difference. Don't forget that iron cookware can add beneficial iron to meals.

Selection Of Airtight Plastic Containers

I've got loads of these ranging from big cereal box-sized ones for storing mixed beans, seeds and nuts, mid-size freezer proof ones for building up a stockpile of meals and smaller ones for storing milled seeds or for snacks and meals for travelling.

KITCHEN EQUIPMENT

*Pistachio nuts are
great for snacking on*

TRAVELLING ON A PLANT-BASED DIET

—

Travelling and following a plant-based diet can be a bit of a minefield. One of the snacks I'll often take to eat at the airport is some crackers and hummus. Sometimes I'm allowed to take it through security but, at other times – despite acknowledging that it's hummus and not plastic explosives – it gets confiscated! On that particular occasion, the situation was compounded by the fact that, once through security, not one of the

"When travelling, supplements can really be useful"

food concessions offered an appealing plant-based meal. Thankfully I had some nuts and seeds with me to see me through! Since then, I've learned what definitely does get through security and I'll tend to take cold nut roast, cold vegetarian pate and snack bars.

The key is to be organised, think ahead and, in a lot of cases, have self-sufficient fallback options.

Even in notoriously carnivorous countries, such as France and Spain, I've usually found that if I just email ahead to hotels and restaurants with my nutritional needs, rather than just turning up, they're incredibly accommodating. I've also definitely noticed in my travels throughout Europe in the last couple of years that the options for people following plant-based diets have massively increased.

I'd still recommend taking some 'emergency rations' with you though whenever you travel. Top of my list would be a bag of pistachio nuts: I'd have these on me for general snacking but they're also great as a fallback.

It's also when travelling that supplements can really be useful. If you're unsure of what you'll be able to eat, the belt and braces approach of a multivitamin/mineral can be a good idea. Individual sachets of vegan recovery mixes can also be lifesavers and can effectively be meal replacements if you're really struggling to find something suitable.

Get well-stocked with herbs and spices to maximise flavour

- SUMMARY -
THE PLANT-BASED KITCHEN

Making Life Easier

Whether you're eating a plant-based diet or not, eating a healthy and balanced diet requires a bit of planning, effort and organisation. However, once you get into the flow of things and build up a decent store cupboard and bank of recipes, it's really not that difficult.

Could I Make A Meal?

Think about what you have in your larder, fridge and freezer. Could you make yourself a nutritious meal right now? If you can answer yes and ideally also have a meal plan for the rest of the week, you're doing well.

Kit & Gadgets

I love my gadgets and, especially if you struggle to fit in cooking along with work, family, training and other commitments, they can definitely make your life easier. However, they're not essential for successfully following a plant-based diet.

Think Ahead When Travelling

Travelling when following a plant-based diet has definitely become easier in the last few years but it still pays to think ahead and be organised. Get into the habit of emailing ahead to hotels and restaurants and packing some 'emergency rations' just in case.

It doesn't matter how you cook as long as it smells and tastes great

07

THE PLANT-BASED KITCHEN

—

RECIPES

Recipes

———

Some tasty snacks and salads to get you started.

Vegetarian Friendly

RICE BALLS WRAPPED IN SEAWEED

—

Ingredients
5 balls

100g short-grain rice
100g quinoa
200ml water
1 tbsp. soy sauce
100g tofu
10g nori (raw, dried seaweed) sheets
Optional: a dash of chilli sauce (such as Tabasco, Korean chilli paste or habanero sauce)

Like all good recipes, I developed this from borrowing ideas from people I met on my travels and this is a real East-meets-West fusion. When I was a student, I had a Japanese housemate and he would mix leftover rice with an egg, soy sauce and sugar and wrap it all in seaweed. He said that this was traditional travel food in Japan. From a plant-based point of view, this idea is super versatile. I make this as travel food but also for fuelling on the bike as well.

Method

Add the rice, quinoa and water to a pan (or rice cooker) and cook until ready (you can use leftovers from the previous night). When cold, add the soy sauce (many soy sauces are also vegan friendly, just check the label): I also like a dash of chilli sauce, such as Tabasco, Korean chilli paste or habanero sauce. Chop the tofu into really small pieces and add to the rice and quinoa mix. With clean hands gently mix together with your fingers. Shape into an egg-size ball and lay out a sheet of the seaweed. Place the ball in the middle and using wet hands wrap with sheet of seaweed around the ball. Wrap in foil for eating on the bike or in an airtight clear container to take on your travels.

Nutritional Breakdown

MACRO STATS	PER 100g BALL
CALORIES	*148*
CARBOHYDRATE	*25g*
PROTEIN	*6.3g*
FAT	*2g*

Vegetarian Friendly

HUMMUS & MULTIGRAIN CRACKERS

—

Ingredients
1 portion

100g of hummus (shop bought)
3 multigrain crackers or gluten-free
vegan-friendly multigrain crackers
(approx. 33g)
1 teaspoon of toasted cumin seeds
Zest and juice of 1 lemon

This is a one of my go-to super simple snack meals that involves zero effort or prep. I haven't included a scratch recipe for hummus because, even though I have made my own in the past and will again, I find it's so easy and cheap to buy. I use this as my main travel meal; I've learnt that to ensure I do not get it confiscated at security at the airport I will put it into a 100ml container. For variety I will take a few olives as well.

Method
Simply spread the hummus onto the crackers, top with cumin seeds and the zest and juice of the lemon and enjoy! For air travel, make sure you limit the hummus to 100g portions and put it in clear 100ml containers.

Nutritional Breakdown

MACRO STATS	PER 100g	PER 133g SERVING (THREE CRACKERS WITH HUMMUS)
CALORIES	*320*	*426*
CARBOHYDRATE	*20g*	*26g*
PROTEIN	*8.6g*	*11g*
FAT	*21g*	*28g*

Vegetarian Friendly

MIXED BEAN SALAD

—

Ingredients
1-2 portions

10ml olive oil
50g shallots
100g fresh green beans
100g mangetout peas
100g edamame beans (defrosted)
100g red kidney (tinned)
Half a bunch of parsley, chopped
(approx. 10g)
1 red chilli, diced
1 tbsp. of red wine vinegar
1 tsp. of fennel seeds

You can eat this recipe hot or cold. When I'm traveling, I will tend to make it the night before, have a portion then and put the rest in an airtight container and take it with me. It combines fresh and tinned ingredients. You can add a bit more protein by including some tofu or chopped nuts that add a nice crunch. If you're vegan, check the providence of your red wine vinegar to ensure it's made using vegan-friendly red wine. This can be served hot or cold.

Method
Sauté the shallots in the olive oil until soft then add the beans and gently stir-fry until soft. Toss in the chopped parsley, diced chilli, red wine vinegar and fennel seeds, season well with salt and pepper.

Nutritional Breakdown

MACRO STATS	PER 100g	PER 300g SERVING
CALORIES	*75*	*225*
CARBOHYDRATE	*5.9g*	*16.7g*
PROTEIN	*5.1g*	*15.3g*
FAT	*3.4g*	*10.2g*

PLANT-BASED RIDE DAYS

—

How to put it all into practice to fuel
your ride and performance.

- CHAPTER 8 -

PLANT-BASED RIDE DAYS

—

In this chapter we'll bring everything we've discussed so far together into practical guidelines for fuelling your rides and ensuring optimum recovery. There will be some repetition and, with regards to the specific macronutrients, carbohydrates, proteins and fats, you might want to refer back to their specific relevant chapters. However in this chapter you'll find a quick and easy go-to guide for a plant-based approach to those big days out on the bike, including a number of recipes.

We'll start with the day before, move onto breakfast, look at fuelling on the bike and then move onto post-ride nutrition and rest days. The main focus of the chapter will be on how you would approach a sportive or long training ride but we'll also look at some specific racing scenarios such as early morning time trials, mid-morning cyclo-cross and evening circuit races and track leagues.

> "Make the difference between pleasurable ride or miserable slog"

The key, as with all aspects of cycling nutrition, is to remember that we're all individuals: so what might be the perfect fuelling strategy for one rider, might not be quite right for you. Base your strategy on the guidelines in this book but then practice and refine them during your training rides. Get it nailed down in training, maybe making a few mistakes, but have it 100% set in stone for important events. In professional cycling, fuelling is critical to ensure optimal performance but, at all levels of the sport, getting it right can make the difference between a pleasurable ride or a miserable slog.

→

*Everyone is different so experiment
to find what works best for you*

Up your carbs by about 25% per meal in the days before the event

THE DAY BEFORE

———

What you eat on the day before a big event or training ride plays a massive role in how you'll perform the next day. You're laying the nutritional foundations for your efforts tomorrow and ensuring that your body's energy stores – in the form of glycogen stores in your muscles and liver – are fully topped up.

The past wisdom for preparing for endurance events was a convoluted routine of carbohydrate depletion followed by gorging yourself at pre-event pasta parties. Many amateur athletes even skipped the depletion phase and just saw it as an excuse for a massive pasta binge. This just isn't necessary or effective and will tend to result in unnecessary fat storage and a feeling of being bloated and sluggish the next day – hardly conducive to a good ride. Some riders make the opposite mistake. With a light day, complete rest or travel before an event, they cut back on their eating too much and manage to deplete their energy stores.

In the lead up to a big ride that you want to perform optimally on, you should have tapered your training down and be well recovered. Because of this drop in workload, as long as you have been eating well, your muscle glycogen levels will have naturally risen to near full capacity. This replenishment of your body's energy stores, particularly if you had previously been training hard, is often accompanied by a 1-2kg weight gain. This often stresses riders out, even experienced pros, but it's down to

the fact that for every 1g of glycogen, the body will also take on 4g of water. This weight gain should be seen as a good sign that your body is ready for a big day out. On the day before therefore, the emphasis should be on quality, not quantity, managing blood sugar levels and not creating any digestive distress.

Although you don't need massive plates of pasta, you should aim to increase your carbohydrate intake slightly. A good rule of thumb is that you should up it by about 25% each meal in the 24-48 hours before a big ride. If it's just a training ride, you could probably limit that increase to your final evening meal if you were at all concerned about overeating.

If you're following a plant-based diet, it's likely that your usual carbohydrate sources are super healthy, unrefined and heavy in bulk and fibre. This is great most of the time but, in the lead up to an important ride – especially if you're looking to up your carbohydrate intake and minimise the risk of mid-ride 'convenience stops' – fibre intake should be reduced and you should opt for more refined carbohydrate sources such as white basmati rice, white bread and potatoes. A more extreme version of this approach is to switch to a Low Residue-type diet (see Chapter 5, starts on p124), which a growing number of riders in the pro peloton are now doing. It can help clear out 1-2kg of matter from your digestive tract, further reduce the risk of a toilet stop and make for improved comfort in aggressive riding positions. However, it doesn't suit all and should be tested in training first. You can also use carbohydrate drinks to increase your energy intake without additional bulk and these can be especially useful to sip on if you have a long drive the day before an event.

Try to avoid heavily spiced meals or any foods that you're unfamiliar with and haven't eaten pre-ride before. The night before an important event isn't the time for gastronomic experimentation. Alcohol is another no-no and, although this may sound obvious, many riders, myself included, have succumbed to a pint or two the night before. The nerves and excitement of a big ride the next day and maybe being away from home and in a hotel, make a calming drink seem like a good idea. One drink probably won't make a difference but it's all too easy for one to lead to more. Alcohol can have a negative impact on your body's ability to synthesise and store glycogen, reduce hydration levels, prevent full restful sleep and can leave you feeling groggy the next day. You've probably trained hard; don't waste all that effort for the sake of a few drinks, save raising a glass for celebrating the evening after. It can also be a good idea to cut back on caffeine for a few days before a key event. It'll help you to sleep well the night before and will cause you to get a bit more of a boost from any caffeine you do consume on the day.

Most plant-based quality protein sources, such a soya and tofu, are well tolerated, easily digested and are fine to consume the day before. It's important to keep up a good protein intake as this will maintain your

amino acid pool and help to ensure optimal recovery from the ride. Healthy fats should also be consumed in normal amounts, as these will provide an additional valuable fuel source for the ride.

Unlike pros who, apart from the very longest races, such as Milan-San Remo, tend to start racing at a very civilised hour of about 11am, many sportives have very early starts and, the earlier you're riding at, the more impactful your nutrition the day before is. I've done sportives that roll off at 6am and this isn't uncommon. If you are riding this early, you're unlikely to be able to, or want to, eat a full breakfast and so, what you do the day and evening before, becomes even more crucial. For really early starts, you might want to consider moving your main evening meal earlier and then adding another lighter meal, such as some cereal and non-dairy milk or some soya milk rice pudding, an hour or so before you go to bed.

"Good sleep hygiene is really important before a ride"

Just before turning in, some tart cherry juice can be beneficial. The melatonin it contains can aid sleep and the fructose (fruit sugar) will provide a good final top up for your glycogen stores. Another supplement that claims to enhance and improve sleep is 5-Hydroxytryptophan (5-HTP). Also known as oxitriptan, it is a naturally occurring form of the essential amino acid tryptophan and is involved in the biosynthesis of the neurotransmitter serotonin. Serotonin is then crucial in the synthesis of melatonin, which is known as the 'sleep hormone'. There is not a great evidence base for the use of 5-HTP, however I know a lot of people who use it

Ideally, allow four hours between breakfast and the start

and feel benefits regarding helping them to get to sleep. That said, don't take 5-HTP if you're taking anti-depressants (among other contraindications) as side effects can include nightmares and very vivid dreams.

Along with nutrition, good sleep hygiene is really important before an important ride, especially if you're staying in a hotel. Avoid excessive screen time in the hour before going to bed, turn the TV off at the plug so there's no red standby light and always pack an eye mask and earplugs, especially if you're sharing a room.

A final top travel tip that all the pros use, whether flying or on the bus, is to use compression clothing. Either go for below the knee stockings or full leg tights but ensure they're medical grade and offer a graduated fit. They help blood return to your heart and stop your legs feeling bloated and heavy.

I wear them for the whole journey and remove them once I arrive. There are many sports brands but if you are on a budget the cheaper medical stockings are just as good. When I fly, even if it is a short flight, I always wear them and I feel much better for it.

*A light breakfast is ideal and
should help you go the distance*

BREAKFAST

—

Despite having eaten well the day before, when you wake up, your body is inevitably in a slightly depleted state. Even though you've been asleep, your body has still been using energy. During the night, your brain is still active and glucose is needed to fuel this nocturnal activity. The glycogen stores in your liver are primarily there to maintain blood glucose levels and, as you sleep, you'll steadily tap these reserves. As previously mentioned, some cherry juice at bedtime can help to offset this a bit. The priority then is to ensure that these stores are restocked. To do this you don't need to have a massive breakfast, which is good news if you struggle to eat first thing in the morning, but equally, don't go too light as this could cause you to have doubts about whether you'll have enough energy in the tank.

You'll also probably wake up a bit dehydrated so don't forget hydration. You should have been drinking well yesterday so don't over drink in the morning or you'll be forced into an early comfort break.

> *"To restock stores you don't need a massive breakfast"*

Sip continuously and aim to consume about 500ml per hour in the lead up to a ride. If you struggle to eat before a ride, you can use a sport drink to help ensure you are getting enough carbohydrates.

If you don't use a carbohydrate based sports drink, it's worth adding some electrolytes to your water. The sodium will help the absorption of the water and also reduce the amount that is just excreted as urine. Of course, you can buy electrolyte tabs, which are very popular, or you can make your own. My recipe for this (see p228) is one that I have used a lot of times when I have been away with riders and wanted something simpler than commercial hydration drinks. An additional benefit to this modular approach is that you can double the water if you want it to be less concentrated. The recipe's formulation provides very similar amounts of sodium to many commercial carbohydrate energy drink products. Another popular alternative is coconut water, which contains many natural electrolytes including potassium.

BEFORE THE RIDE

—

With the pros and their late 11am starts, we'll work back from the start of the ride and aim to have breakfast three to four hours before they set off. They'll then snack through to the start, following a similar routine as to how they feed on the bike. It's essential that their breakfast is fully digested as the first hour or so of racing is often very intense until the day's break is established.

However, as we've previously discussed, sportives often don't have such civilised start times and, even for a typical Sunday club run, you're normally looking at a 9am meet-up. So, assuming you've eaten well the day before (maybe including a pre-bed snack), just how late can you push that start time? There are three main factors to consider; what you eat, ride intensity and your personal digestive tolerance.

For the first factor, if you make breakfast super-easy to digest, it's perfectly reasonable to eat it up until an hour before heading out. Anything based around rice, such as soya rice pudding or rice mixed with soya yoghurt, would be ideal.

Most sportives and club runs don't go off super-fast. The only exception would be a sportive that goes straight into a hard climb. Do some research on the route and, if you know it'll be a steady start, again you can push your breakfast window forwards.

Finally, is individual preference. This has to be tested in training. Try some of the easier to digest rice-based breakfasts and see how close to training rides you can tolerate them. Once you've found a timing and breakfast that works for you, apply it to events.

As a general rule of thumb, for a long ride, you should be looking to consume 1g of carbohydrate per kilogram of bodyweight for your breakfast. The breakfast recipes in this chapter (see p224-p227 all deliver 60-70g of carbohydrate so, if you're bigger than this, you might want to increase the quantities slightly. You should also aim to have about 20g of protein and some fat. Soya milk is a complete protein source and you can also stir in some vegan protein powder into your breakfast. For the fat, stirring in some coconut oil is a great way to obtain this and to up the energy content of your breakfast.

For many cyclists, a coffee is an essential part of their pre-ride ritual. There's certainly no harm in including a couple of single shot espressos with your breakfast, which will give you about 100mg of caffeine. This will give you a bit of a lift, especially if you've abstained for a couple of days beforehand, and there's some evidence that it can also improve your ability to utilise fat as a fuel. It can also help to ensure that you have a bowel movement before heading out.

> "Consider ride intensity and your digestive tolerance"

FLAP JACK

RICE CAKE

RICE CAKE

Don't forget to get all your on-the-bike nutrition ready, too

ON THE BIKE

—

For a typical sportive or long training ride, you're likely to be out riding for three to six hours or more. Eat well the day before and follow the breakfast advice previously to ensure you've laid down some solid nutritional foundations. Although you're likely to be predominately riding fairly steadily to pace the long effort, there will be more intensity on significant climbs.

My go-to on the bike snack will always be rice cakes but there is a whole range of options to try. Bananas are great, paninis with nut butter and jam and, for a savoury option, Japanese-style rice balls with tofu (see p186 for their recipes). On long rides, you want the slower burn energy from 'real food' choices and they'll also help to prevent your stomach feeling empty. Save the gels for when you need a quick energy burst. Don't forget that your bottles can also provide fuel, with a regular sports fuel typically providing about 20g of carbohydrate per 500ml. As discussed in Chapter 3 (starts on p78), some modern sports drinks can provide up to 80g per 500ml bottle and provide all of your fuelling needs.

As a general plan, stick to the advice given in Chapter 3; on any ride over 90 minutes in duration, you should be looking to take on between 0.5-1g/kg of bodyweight of carbohydrates per hour. Where you fuel within that range will be

"Try products in training to check that you tolerate them"

determined by individual needs, intensity and duration of the ride. In simple terms, the longer and harder you're riding, the more fuel you'll need.

Although carbohydrates will be primarily fuelling the ride, if it's over four hours, you should also be looking to take some protein on board. By taking on approximately 20g mid-ride or accumulating that amount throughout the ride, you'll improve post-ride recovery, spare lean tissue damage and feel fuller and less hungry. The Japanese style rice balls with tofu are really good for getting some protein in.

The key though is to eat early, little and often. Right from the start of any long ride, you should be aiming to eat something every 20-30 minutes – don't wait until you feel hungry. You're not eating for that moment but 15-30km down the road. It's worth setting a reminder on your bike computer, watch or taping a note to your stem. Even pro riders do this as, in the excitement of a race, they'll forget to eat. It's really unpleasant and difficult to dig yourself out of a blood sugar crash so avoid it by eating little, early and often throughout the ride.

Do some research on the route as, in addition to your regular feeds, if there are some significant climbs it can be a good idea to have a gel five minutes before

No matter how long your ride, eating a little and often is key

hitting its base. Even if you've taken on some regular food fairly recently, a gel can still give you a much-needed boost for the higher intensity climbing effort. Just the act of having a sugary substance in your mouth will give you an initial lift and then, as you climb, the fast release carbohydrates will kick in. As we discussed in Chapter 3 (starts on p78), in your mouth there are receptors that detect the 'sweet' taste from the gel and sends a signal to the brain that there is carbohydrate on its way. This in itself can give a performance boost before the energy has even hit the blood stream. Depending on the length of the climb, you might also want to take a feed as you go over the top. You won't be working hard as you descend and this makes it far easier for your body to digest and absorb food. Watch any pro race in the mountains and you'll see the riders fuelling up in this way as they crest any major climb.

On most sportives you'll have a number of feed stations but my advice is to try to not rely and them and be as independent about your nutrition as possible. All it takes is for the event organiser's logistics to be slightly out and you could be rolling into a feed station with nothing but banana skins left. Also, if you're following a strict plant-based diet, it's impossible to know whether the various cakes and flapjacks on offer are suitable for you. Even for a four to six hour ride, it's not too difficult to carry all the food you'll need and that way you know you won't miss out. If you do decide to use the feed stations, do some research before the event about where they're situated and what they're offering. Make sure you try the products that'll be used in training to check that you tolerate them. I'd still recommend carrying a stash of your own gels for climbs, in case you have a sugar crash or if a feed station lets you down.

- HYDRATION & RIDING IN THE HEAT -

Over the last few years, there's been a lot of confusion and misinformation about hydration and endurance sports. Horror stories about water intoxication (a potentially fatal condition caused by the excessive intake of water pushing the body's normal balance of electrolytes outside safe limits) or hyponatremia (low blood sodium concentrations which, at worst, can induce a coma) have scared athletes into drinking less but, as long as you're consuming electrolytes with the fluids, the risks of drinking too little massively outweigh the dangers of consuming too much.

Electrolytes are supplied by sports drink mixes, dissolvable tablets and from the food you consume on the bike. So, there should be no issue obtaining enough of them to balance your fluid intake. In normal riding conditions – up to about 25°C – I'll encourage riders to consume at least one 500ml bottle every hour. In higher temperatures, this could easily rise to two to three bottles but, as long as their electrolyte intake was sufficient, any excess would be safely excreted.

As with eating, little, early and often is the approach to take to drinking. Just get into the habit of taking a decent sip from your bottle every 10-15 minutes from the start of your ride and you won't go far wrong. It really is that simple.

Obviously, you won't be able to carry enough liquid for your entire ride and you will be reliant on feed stations or stops to refill your bottles. Again, check which sports drink they're using and try it in training. Alternatively, bag up some of your own tried and tested sports drink powder in bidon portions and make this up with plain water from the feed stations.

A common reason for riders suffering from gastric distress and underperforming, especially when riding abroad, is that they're not acclimated to the heat. You've invested a lot of time and effort in preparation and probably money too for entry, flights and accommodation so neglecting this key factor is really shortsighted. It's really easy, in the weeks leading up to such an event, to set your turbo up in your bathroom or conservatory, heat it up to 30°C and achieve some really significant acclimatisation. You only need to do eight to 10 hour-long sessions and these can include double session days. If you think you're likely to experience temperatures exceeding 35°C, it's worth seeking professional advice as to a safe and effective protocol.

*Try to get into the habit of
sipping every 10-15 minutes*

POST-RIDE

—

There's no denying that post-ride nutrition is important but, depending on a number of factors, it isn't necessarily the make or break scenario that it's often (usually by sports nutrition companies) portrayed to be. There are really only two main aspects of recovery that you need to consider from a nutritional perspective: muscular and metabolic.

Muscular recovery is about rebuilding and repairing muscles that have been damaged and stressed by exercise. When we exercise, we actually cause some of the proteins within our own bodies to start to break down and this is known as a catabolic response. Once we finish exercising we're in a state where our bodies can rebuild and extend these proteins. This process is referred to as an anabolic phase. In Chapter 1 (starts p32) we discussed how, for endurance athletes, this process is primarily concerned with producing the energy-producing powerhouses of cells, mitochondria. To fuel this muscular recovery, quality protein is required and this, rather than just carbohydrates, should be the priority post-ride. A 20g serving of vegan protein powder mixed in 500ml of water is ideal.

Metabolic recovery is primarily concerned with restocking your body's carbohydrate and energy stores. It also involves the muscle restocking their intramuscular fat that may have been used during the ride. There is not a special nutritional application for this, as general post exercise re-feeding will take care of it. You'll often hear about a golden window of opportunity up to 30 minutes post exercise, where your body will hoover up any carbohydrates you provide and maximise your glycogen stores. The muscles have a limited capacity to store glycogen and the transport of carbohydrate into them is dependent on 'transporters' being activated; these transporters are called Glute 4 transporters and are activated by insulin and/or vigorous exercise. This is why, post exercise, if the muscle is depleted it can be most readily refilled. The problem is that the studies that showed this used protocols that totally depleted the subjects' glycogen stores. If you have followed the advice above and fuelled well, even after a long ride, you shouldn't be finishing in a completely depleted state. Therefore, there's no massive rush to get loads of carbohydrates into your system and, as long as you'll be eating within the first hour or so, additional carbohydrates above what you'll get from this meal shouldn't be necessary. As covered in Chapter 3 (starts p78), for 90-120 minutes of steady riding, this meal should give you 1g/kg of body weight but after a long and hard day in the saddle that could rise to 1.5g/kg. Where getting the carbohydrates in quicker is important is if you're riding again the following day or are doing a double session day. Also, if you have misfuelled or really emptied your tank on a finishing climb, getting those carbohydrates in as quickly as possible would be advisable.

> "Recovery is about rebuilding and repairing muscles"

A protein recovery drink followed by a good meal is ideal

- DO I NEED A RECOVERY DRINK? -

Most commercially available recovery drinks deliver both carbohydrates and protein and there's now an increasing range of such products that are suitable for riders following a plant-based diet. Using one can be a good idea and, if you're jumping straight in the car or won't be eating for a couple of hours, is undeniably convenient. Also, if you're doing a multi-day event or a training camp, kick-starting both metabolic and muscular recovery is important. However, if you are able to eat within a reasonable one to two hour time window, a carbohydrate and protein recovery drink is likely to be overkill and will just result in unnecessary calories. Have your protein drink straight away but use your next meal to top up your carbohydrates. This is how I work with the pros, giving them a protein drink straight away and then they'll have a rice-based recovery meal once back on the team bus.

Different time trial distances require differing fuelling strategies

EARLY MORNING TIME-TRIAL

Many time trials have early morning starts, often before 8am. This isn't just a tradition that harks back to the days when the sport was frowned upon by the authorities and conducted in secret but is due to the lower early morning traffic volume. This obviously can create issues for timing your breakfast as, especially for longer events, you'll need to be well fuelled. These difficulties are often compounded by a lengthy drive to the event.

If you are pressed for breakfast, an ideal option is the soya milk rice pudding (see the recipe for this on p227). You could easily eat this in a lay-by in your car up to about an hour before your start time.

For a 25 mile event, consuming approximately 20g-40g of carbohydrates, maybe in the form of a gel and a caffeinated gel, during the ride will keep blood sugar levels and focus up. I tend to recommend having a gel at 20 and

40 minutes, with the 40 minute gel being a caffeine gel providing about 50mg of caffeine. For 50 mile events and longer, including 12- and 24-hour, you'll adopt a feeding strategy more akin to that described for a sportive or long training ride.

From a recovery perspective, follow the advice earlier in the chapter (on p206) as to whether a recovery drink containing carbohydrates would be appropriate. However, due to the big gears commonly pushed in time trials, muscular damage can be quite high and therefore post-ride protein intake is definitely important.

Time trialists, especially those targeting longer events, might want to experiment with a low residue diet (see Chapter 5, p124) the day before an event as it can make holding an aerodynamic position more comfortable.

'Cyclo-cross's intensity makes it difficult to fuel during a race'

MID-MORNING CYCLO-CROSS

—

Although the races are only typically 30-60 minutes long, the high intensity nature of the racing, along with time spent warming up and riding practice laps, means that you have to be well fuelled.

Races will normally start at 10-11am so, working back, having breakfast at 7-8am allows plenty of time for digestion and any of the porridge options (see p224) would be ideal. With so long until the start of the race though, another snack, such as a banana or an energy bar, about an hour before your start time and sipping on a sports drink will keep you ticking over.

As you can't take on fuel during a cyclo-cross race, some riders like to take a gel, often caffeinated, during their warm-up. Recovery will follow the same advice as for a time trial but bear in mind that you'll probably be finishing fairly close to lunchtime.

Keep your energy topped up in between races

EVENING CLUB 10, CIRCUIT RACE OR TRACK LEAGUE

A club 10 mile time trial or circuit race will typically start between 6-8pm in the evening and during the week. Both are fairly short with a club 10 mile taking most riders between 20-30 minutes and a circuit race 30-45 minutes. However, as with cyclo-cross, you also need to factor in 20 minutes or so of warm up.

Work back from your start time and have a pre-race meal three to four hours beforehand. Something rice-based would be ideal. About an hour or so before, have a banana or a bar. A gel, potentially caffeinated but bear in mind the time of day, might be appropriate during your warm up for a circuit race of over 30 minutes but, for shorter durations, won't have any real effect. Maybe consider trying a carbohydrate mouth rinse (see Chapter 3, p90) for shorter events.

Go for a protein drink to kick-start muscular recovery. You can have this as on your cool down, as you ride home or in the car. Don't worry too much about high carbohydrates as you won't have depleted your stores and can easily top them up once you get home.

Once home, you might not want to eat a full meal this late and it could interfere with your sleep. A light snack, such as some cereal, would be ideal.

For a track league, adopt the same approach leading up to the start time but, with four or more short but very intense races during two hours of racing, you'll need to keep yourself topped up. Rice cakes, bananas or sipping on a sports drink between races is an ideal way to do this.

The muscle load and damage from track racing is high so protein is definitely your recovery priority. Although the race meeting will have lasted two hours, the actual time spent riding hard is fairly short and, as you'll have been taking carbohydrates on throughout, shouldn't need any extra straight away. During the session snack on foods such as the rice cakes or flapjacks and remember to keep sipping fluids. You should only need a light snack when you get home, such as some cereal or a smoothie.

A dairy-free chocolate brownie is a great post-event reward

REST DAYS & SOMETHING SWEET

On rest days, if you're not trying to lose weight, don't cut back your calorie intake too much. You're not going to be taking on the fuel that you normally would when riding and, in reality, your breakfast and lunch on a rest day are likely to be slightly smaller. It's important to remember that a rest day is about recovery and replenishment and, if you're under fuelled, this isn't going to occur. If you are trying to lose a few kilos, cut the amount of carbohydrates you're consuming by about 20%, especially during your evening meal.

> "It can be great to have something sweet waiting as a reward"

Something Sweet

A lot of riders like to have something sweet occasionally and eating a plant-based diet does not mean that you have to give up on the occasional treat, especially if you're not trying to lose weight. It can be great to have something waiting as a reward after a hard ride, as a pick me up in the car after an event or just with your after dinner coffee. If you've got some spare time on a rest day, why not see my dessert recipes for inspiration (starting on p227 with soya milk rice pudding).

- SUMMARY -
PLANT-BASED RIDE DAYS

Practice, Refine & Implement

Whether it's for a local sportive or a Grand Tour, all riders should practice their fuelling strategies in training, refine them to their own individual tastes and needs and then implement them – without compromise or deviation – on event day.

The Day Before

Keep it simple, digestible and stick to tried and tested favourites. Depending on the length, intensity and importance of the event, increase your carbohydrate intake by 25% at each meal for 24-48 hours beforehand. If you're going to be travelling, plan ahead and, if it's a really early start, consider an additional pre-bed snack.

Breakfast

Work back from your start time and ideally allow three to four hours. However, if this isn't realistic and, depending on the ride's starting intensity and your breakfast choice, this can be squeezed to an hour. Aim to consume 1g of carbohydrate per kilogram of bodyweight and 20g total of protein. Stirring in coconut oil is a great way to give your breakfast a performance lifting fat boost!

On The Bike

Little, early and often. Don't wait until you're feeling hungry or weak. On any ride over 90 minutes in duration, you should be looking to take on between 0.5-1g/kg of bodyweight of carbohydrates per hour. On rides of over four to five hours, you should also look to take on 20g of protein.

Hydration

Keep it simple and, as long as you're taking in electrolytes, don't worry about over drinking. Aim to consume between 500ml and 1l per hour depending on conditions. If you get into the habit of reaching for your bottle every 10 minutes or so, your body will do a decent job of regulating your intake.

Right: Remember, you're not fuelling for now but 15-30km down the road

Bottom: Don't wait until you're thirsty or hungry — by then it's already too late

08

PLANT-BASED
RIDE DAYS

—

Before The Ride

On The Ride

Post-Ride

Something Sweet

Discover delicious and nutritionally-balanced food to fuel your ride.

Vegetarian Friendly

QUORN BOLOGNESE SAUCE

___

Ingredients
3 portions

15ml (1 tbsp.) olive oil
150g chopped onion
4 cloves garlic (approx. 6g)
1 bunch of rosemary, chopped
1 tsp. fennel seeds
400g (1 tin) chopped canned tomatoes
15ml (1 tbsp.) tomato puree
2 bay leaves
50g red lentils
200g Quorn mince
Salt and pepper

Quorn (or other grain or soy-based vegemince) is ideal for using in Bolognese-style sauces. This modern incarnation of the traditional Italian sauce is really a distant cousin of the Bologna signature dish but is still delicious and nutritious. Serve with egg-free pasta, rice or the mixed grains below. If you're vegan, use vegan grain or soy-based mince and gluten-free tomato puree.

Method
Sauté the onions, garlic, chopped rosemary and fennel seeds in a large heavy-bottom saucepan over a medium heat. When soft (roughly six minutes), add the tinned tomatoes, tomato puree, bay leaves and lentils, simmer for approximately 20 minutes stirring occasionally to ensure consistent cooking and prevent burning (if it becomes thick add approximately 100ml of extra water). Add the Quorn mince and stir in. Cook for a further 10-15 minutes and have a taste to make sure that the lentils are soft. Season with salt and pepper.

Nutritional Breakdown

MACRO STATS	PER 100g	PER SERVING (280g)
CALORIES	*86*	*241*
CARBOHYDRATE	*7.9g*	*22g*
PROTEIN	*5.3g*	*15.5g*
FAT	*2.9g*	*8.4g*

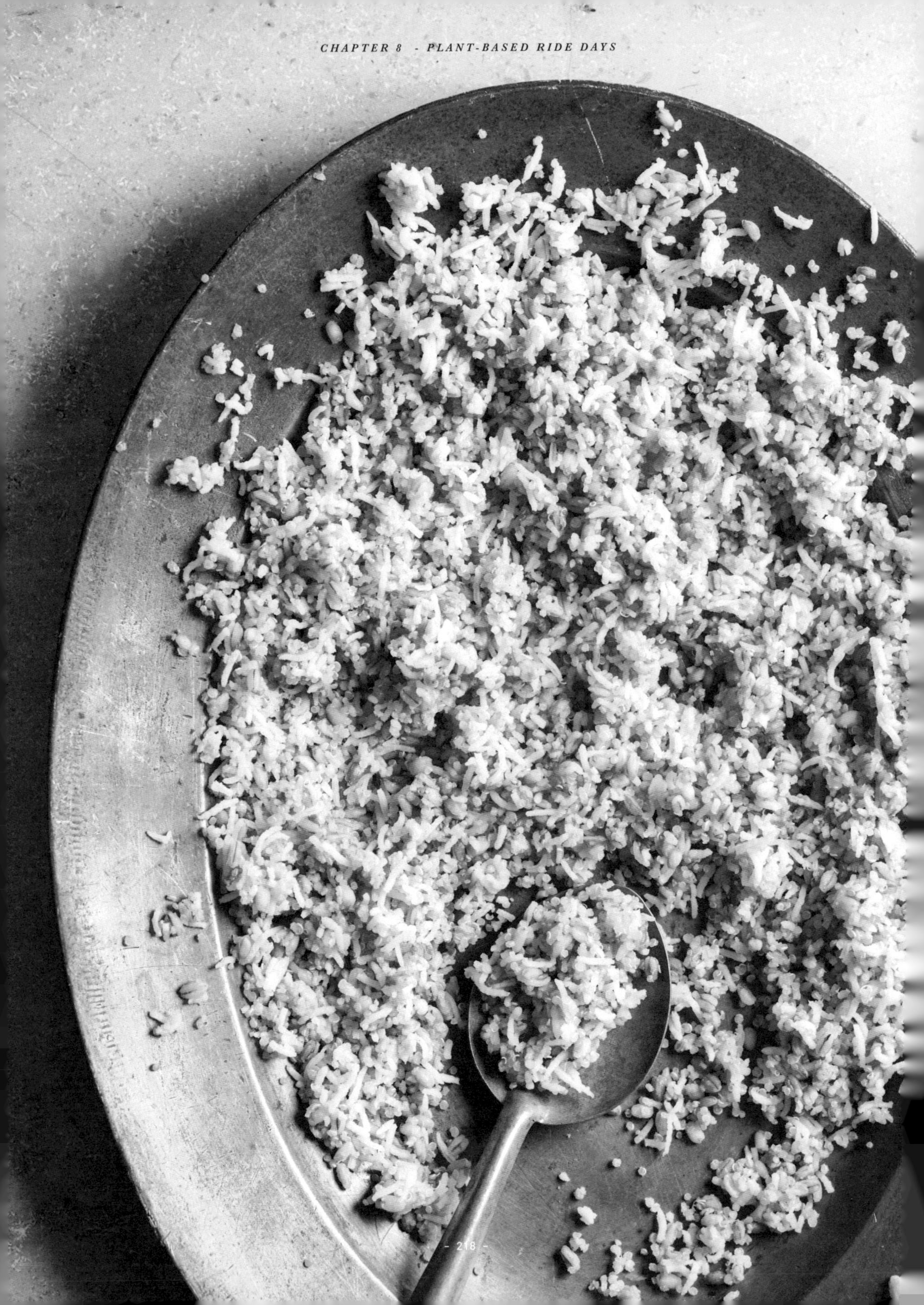

Vegan & Vegetarian Friendly

MIXED GRAINS

—

Ingredients
4-5 portions

100g pearl barley
100g quinoa
100g basmati rice
100g pearl spelt
800ml water

This is a real staple of mine and I tend to batch cook it and put portions into airtight 'vac-pac' bags to eat later. I find combining the different grains provides really great texture, taste and nutrition.

Method
Wash the grains, drain and place all of the ingredients into a rice cooker and cook according to your machine's instructions. If using a pan, place all ingredients into the pan, bring to heat and then simmer (keeping covered) until all of the water is absorbed (about 15 minutes).

Nutritional Breakdown

MACRO STATS	PER 100g	PER SERVING (300g)
CALORIES	*113*	*339*
CARBOHYDRATE	*22g*	*66g*
PROTEIN	*3.8g*	*11.4g*
FAT	*0.8g*	*2.4g*

Vegetarian Friendly

TOFU RISOTTO

Ingredients
4 portions

30g dried porcini mushrooms
400g (1 block) tofu (raw)
20g (approx. 2 square cm) ginger
1 tbsp. soy sauce
2 medium onions (approx. 150g)
100g chopped leeks
3 garlic cloves
2 tbsp. olive oil
100g Arborio risotto rice
100g quinoa
100g pearl barley
100g pearled spelt
400g (1 tin) canned coconut milk
100g frozen edamame beans
100g frozen peas
3 vegetable stock cubes

Risotto has always been one of cyclists' favourite meals but traditional non-plant-based ones tend to be heavy in dairy. This plant-based version is not only delicious but really nutritious and lighter on the stomach. The tinned coconut milk gives it a really rich texture and mouth feel. I use mixed grains which again have got great texture and nutrition.

Method

Soak the dried mushrooms in boiling water (approx. 300ml) for about 30 minutes before cooking. Cut the tofu into cubes approximately 2cm x 2cm x 2cm, marinade in a little soy sauce (many soy sauces are also vegan friendly, just check the label to be sure) and chopped ginger. Fry the tofu until it is a light golden brown (top tip: use an air dryer as it crisps tofu up brilliantly). Chop the onion, leek and garlic and lightly fry in the olive oil. When soft, add the mixed grains and cook gently as they absorb the fluid from the onions etc., add the soaked dried mushrooms including the water, add the tinned coconut milk and the rest of the ingredients. Simmer gently for about 20 minutes or until the grains are soft. Add extra water if needed. Season with salt and pepper and top off with the cooked tofu. Great served with steamed asparagus and baby sweetcorn on the side.

Nutritional Breakdown

MACRO STATS	PER 100g	PER SERVING (400g)
CALORIES	*170*	*680*
CARBOHYDRATE	*20g*	*80g*
PROTEIN	*6g*	*24g*
FAT	*7.1g*	*28.4g*

Vegetarian Friendly

MIXED BEAN CHILLI

—

Ingredients
4-5 portions

2 litres (3 ½ pints) of water
6-7 medium onions (approx. 480g)
800g tinned tomatoes
200g whole blackeye beans, dried
200g butter beans, dried
200g red kidney beans, dried
100g pinto beans, dried
50g tomato puree
1 vegetable stock cube
Optional: 1 tsp. chilli powder
Optional: 1 tsp. smoked paprika
Optional: 1 tsp. ground cumin
Optional: 1 tsp. mixed herbs

This is one of my family's absolute favourites, so much so that I always make a big batch so we can have it twice a week! It's also great served cold as a lunch or a travel food.

Method
This can be cooked in a slow cooker or pressure cooker.

Slow Cooker Method
Chop or dice the onions and then put all the ingredients in the pot to soak overnight and switch the slow cooker on its medium setting in the morning; this will take about 8-12 hours. Remember to stir occasionally.

Electric Pressure Cooker Method
Again, chop or dice the onions. You can cook the beans from dry but I find if I soak them overnight they cook a little better. I use an electric pressure cooker and I will set the cooking time for 40 minutes at high pressure (in total the cooking time is about 1 hour 20 minutes – this includes the heating up and then the natural decompression time after cooking). On most electric pressure cookers there is a timer function so you can set it for the food to be ready after training.

Nutritional Breakdown

MACRO STATS	PER 100g	PER 440g SERVING
CALORIES	*71*	*331*
CARBOHYDRATE	*11g*	*51g*
PROTEIN	*4.6g*	*21g*
FAT	*0.5g*	*1.9g*

Vegan & Vegetarian Friendly

QUINOA/AMARANTH PORRIDGE

___

Ingredients
1 portion

50g amaranth and/or quinoa grains
150ml soya milk
4 tsp. coconut oil

I have been using these pseudo-grains for some time; you can use either to make porridge or you can mix them together. Both are complete proteins, which mean they provide all of the body's essential amino acids. You can make porridge with regular quinoa but you can also buy quinoa flakes that can provide a more porridge-like texture and are easier to cook. If you like, you can also flavour these simply with cardamom, cinnamon or vanilla bean paste.

Method

Add the amaranth or quinoa to the soya milk. You can do this step the night before so it's ready to go in the morning. If using a pan, cook on a low heat for about 20 minutes or until the gains have swollen and absorbed the milk. If using a microwave, cook for about 4 minutes, remove, stir and cook for about another 2 minutes and repeat until the grains are swollen and soft. Mix in the coconut oil and serve topped with the goji berry seed mix from Chapter 2 (see recipe on p72).

Nutritional Breakdown

MACRO STATS	PER 100g	PER SERVING (200g)
CALORIES	*145*	*297*
CARBOHYDRATE	*16g*	*33g*
PROTEIN	*5.8g*	*12g*
FAT	*5.8g*	*12g*

Vegetarian Friendly

SOYA MILK RICE PUDDING

Ingredients
2 good portions

200g short grain pudding rice
700ml fortified soya milk
30g (2 tbsp.) sugar (or soft brown sugar)
30g (2 tbsp.) coconut oil
1 teaspoon of vanilla bean seeds or paste
Zest and juice of 1 orange

I am a huge fan of rice-based foods; the structure of the starch makes it really easy on the stomach and it's pretty much fully digestible. A soya milk rice pudding can be a great pre-event meal. You can eat it hot or cold so can easily travel with it. The recipe I use is pretty quick as I just use a rice cooker. If I am feeling posh I add a pinch of saffron. If vegan, use vegan sugar or cane sugar alternatives from beet and coconut.

Method
Place all of the ingredients into a rice cooker and cook according to your machine's instructions. If using a pan add all of the ingredients, bring the contents up to heat and simmer gently for about 30 minutes. Stir regularly and watch for sticking or burning.

Nutritional Breakdown

MACRO STATS	PER 100g	PER SERVING (470g)
CALORIES	*125*	*593*
CARBOHYDRATE	*20g*	*94g*
PROTEIN	*3.4g*	*16g*
FAT	*3.3g*	*16g*

Vegan & Vegetarian Friendly

HOMEMADE HYDRATION DRINK

—

Ingredients
1 portion

500ml water
1g salt (tip: the salt sachets available
from takeaways provide 1g of salt)
Juice and zest of 1 lemon

The energy and hydration drink market is massive but it is really easy to make your own that's both effective and very cheap to do. I've used this for a long time and, if I have riders away on camps that have either not got enough commercial hydration drink or have run out, it's become my go-to recipe.

Method
Simply mix the ingredients above together.

Nutritional Breakdown

MACRO STATS	PER 100g	PER 500ml SERVING
CALORIES	*2*	*10*
CARBOHYDRATE	*0.5g*	*2.5g*
PROTEIN	*0g*	*0g*
FAT	*0g*	*0g*

Vegetarian Friendly

NUT BUTTER & JAM PANINI

—

Ingredients
4 portions

2 small soft white bread rolls (approx. 80g)
2 tbsp. fruit jam (approx. 30g – can be bought!)
2 tbsp. nut butter (approx. 30g)

I know this sounds a bit sad but I make my own jam and, in late summer, I spend hours collecting wild apples and blackberries to make it. I also make my own nut butter (see Chapter 2, recipe on p74) so these paninis can be genuinely homemade. They're great on steadier rides or in the first half of a harder ride or race before things speed up. Even into today's high-tech nutrition world of bars and gels, the traditional panini is still a mainstay food in the pro peloton.

Method
Slice rolls in half and spread the jam on one side and the nut butter on the other. Put the halves together, cut in half and wrap for the ride.

Nutritional Breakdown

MACRO STATS	PER 100g	PER SERVING (36g)
CALORIES	*336*	*121*
CARBOHYDRATE	*47g*	*17g*
PROTEIN	*11g*	*4g*
FAT	*11g*	*4g*

Vegetarian Friendly

RICE CAKES

—

Ingredients
20 portions

500g short grain pudding rice
1 litre (1 ¾ pints) water
200g creamed coconut (block)
30g (2 tbsp.) sugar
1 tsp. vanilla extract
Optional: 1 tsp. cinnamon

I developed this plant-based version of rice cakes because Rigoberto Uran tends to avoid dairy and I had a lot of requests from other riders for a dairy-free version. During races the team will make one dairy-free rice cake and one with creamed cheese. The original rice cakes dates back to Dr Allen Lim (sports physiologist, coach and Skratch Labs founder) when he started using rice cookers in pro cycling. He told me that he used to be made fun of by other teams but now everyone uses rice cookers. I have developed and evolved his original recipes; you can make these without a rice cooker but I don't feel they come out as good. Again, if vegan, you can use vegan sugar or sugar alternatives.

Method

Place all of the ingredients into a rice cooker and cook according to your machine's instructions. When cooked, mix everything together until it is smooth and spoon the hot mixture into a airtight zip fastener freezer bag (size large or medium depending on brand); flatten out to roughly 4cm deep and smooth the air out. Leave to cool on a flat tray. Once cool, refrigerate overnight. Remove carefully from the bag, cut into approximately 20 squares and keep in an airtight container in the fridge. If refrigerated they will keep for about four days. When using on the bike, wrap in silver paper – the best to use is the type that is silver foil on one side with backing parchment on the other.

Nutritional Breakdown

MACRO STATS	PER 100g	PER SERVING OF 1 PIECE
CALORIES PER 100G	*180*	*170*
CARBOHYDRATE	*23g*	*22g*
PROTEIN	*1.3g*	*1.2g*
FAT	*9g*	*8.4g*

ON THE BIKE

Vegetarian Friendly

FLAPJACKS

Ingredients
10 flapjacks

150g coconut oil
90g agave nectar
90g brown sugar
170g oats
75g mixed chopped nuts
75g dried mixed fruit
1 banana, peeled and
mashed with a fork

Flapjacks are a traditional cyclists' favourite, and arguably these plant-based ones are both nutritionally better and tastier than their buttery counterparts. They deliver a great blend of fast acting sugars, slower burn carbohydrates and fat to fuel your ride. Again, if vegan, you can use vegan sugar or sugar alternatives from beet and coconut.

Method

Pre-heat the oven to 160°C (conventional oven)/140°C (fan-assisted oven), or gas mark four. Line a 20cm square baking tin with baking paper. Melt the coconut oil, sugar and agave nectar in a pan over a medium heat. Remove from the heat and tip in the oats, chopped nuts, dried fruit and the mashed banana being careful not to overheat the mixture. Transfer to the tin, packing the mix in with the back of a spoon. Bake for 30-35 minutes until lightly golden and crisp around the edges – again be careful not to over cook. Leave to cool in the tin before slicing into squares. Keep in an airtight container for up to three days – but I can guarantee that they will not last that long!

Nutritional Breakdown

MACRO STATS	PER 100g	PER SERVING (59g)
CALORIES	*490*	*289*
CARBOHYDRATE	*55g*	*33g*
PROTEIN	*7.8g*	*4.6g*
FAT	*26g*	*15g*

234

Vegan & Vegetarian Friendly

ENERGY BALLS/BARS

——

Ingredients
10 portions

100g oats
250g dates, stoned
60g chia seeds
50g agave nectar

Homemade energy balls are really simple to make and, because you've made them yourself, you know exactly what you are putting into them. This simple recipe combines four different ingredients that provide some fast and slowly released energy. The chia seeds also provide great fats.

Method
Blend the oats, dates and chia seeds together in a food processor. Add the agave nectar and blend once more. Roll into balls, place in fridge for 30-60 minutes to firm up and enjoy! These will keep for up to three days in the fridge.

Nutritional Breakdown

MACRO STATS	PER 100g	PER SERVING (46g)
CALORIES	340	156
CARBOHYDRATE	60g	28g
PROTEIN	6.7g	3.1g
FAT	6g	2.8g

Vegetarian Friendly

DIY PLANT-BASED RECOVERY DRINK/ SMOOTHIE

___

Ingredients
1 portion

300ml soya milk
1 large peeled fresh banana
(approx. 120g)
15g unflavoured vegetable protein
1 tbsp. chia seeds
(approx. 15g)

Making a recovery drink can be a really convenient and high impacting way of delivering nutrients. They are particularly useful if you have done a long ride with only a couple of hours before your main meal so you do not really want a big feed. They're also really useful if racing during the evening, at a track league or evening time trial and so, by the time you've finished, it's getting too late for a full meal. This DIY recovery drink uses an unflavoured mixed vegetable protein (many vegan vegetable protein powders are also now available) and I have included fresh fruit and chia seeds. This provides quality protein fats and carbohydrate and is packed full of micronutrients, too.

Method
Put all of the ingredients into a blender and blend until smooth. If you want a bit more carbohydrate, you can add a squirt of agave nectar. Be aware that if this is made up and left in the fridge it may turn brown, so is best to consume fresh.

Nutritional Breakdown

MACRO STATS	PER 100g	PER SERVING (445g)
CALORIES	*66*	*292*
CARBOHYDRATE	*6g*	*26g*
PROTEIN	*5.2g*	*23g*
FAT	*1.9g*	*8.6g*

Vegetarian Friendly

CHOCOLATE BROWNIES

—

Ingredients
16 portions

200g dark chocolate (80%+)
170g self-raising flour
50g light olive oil
230g soya milk, unsweetened
180g golden caster sugar (or soft brown sugar, if preferred)
30g cocoa powder
15g vanilla extract
50g goji berries
Optional: pinch of salt

These are so easy to make and many real brownie recipes can simply be adapted to make them plant-based. A lot people don't realise that a lot of 80% cocoa content chocolate is fully vegan. I first developed this recipe a few years ago for my kids and it always went down well. If vegan, use vegan sugar or cane sugar alternatives.

Method

There are two different methods for making these brownies. Both start with pre-heating your oven to about 160°C and lining a 20cm baking tray with parchment.

Thermomix Method

Use the in-built scales to weigh the ingredients as you put them in. Start with the chocolate and give it a blast at speed six for about 10 seconds or until it becomes a rough powder. Add the rest of the ingredients – except the goji berries – and mix at level six for about 20 seconds, or until you have a smooth mixture. Add the goji berries, put on reverse blade and mix on speed three for a few seconds. Transfer the mixture to the baking tray. Scrape down the bowl to ensure you get as much brownie mix as possible. Cook for about 20-25 minutes, the middle should still be a bit gooey.

Hob Method

Place a heatproof bowl over a pan of simmering water, making sure the base doesn't touch the water. Break 150g of chocolate into the bowl and allow it to melt, then set aside to cool. Now sieve the flour and cocoa powder into a large bowl. Then stir in the sugar, a pinch of salt and add the vanilla extract. Stir in the oil, soya milk and melted chocolate until combined. Roughly chop and stir in the remaining chocolate and the goji berries. Pour the mixture into a prepared tin, spreading it out evenly and then place in the hot oven for 20 to 25 minutes, or until cooked on the outside, but still gooey in the middle.

SOMETHING SWEET

Nutritional Breakdown

MACRO STATS	PER 100g	PER SERVING (62g)
CALORIES	*365*	*227*
CARBOHYDRATE	*42g*	*26g*
PROTEIN	*5.9g*	*3.7g*
FAT	*18g*	*11g*

Vegetarian Friendly

DAIRY-FREE PISTACHIO GELATO

Ingredients
11 portions

100g pistachio nut kernel
(or butter)
400ml coconut milk canned
100g caster sugar
3 cardamom pods, bashed

I first made this as I was really disappointed with the commercial dairy-free ice creams that I had tried. I was amazed with the results as the coconut milk provides a really creamy body and luxurious texture. I gave some to my mother who said it was the best ice cream she'd tasted so as a rule I nearly always have some in my freezer for when the family ask for it! If vegan, use vegan sugar or cane sugar alternatives.

Method

You can use pistachio nut butter instead of the kernels. If using kernels add to a powerful food processor and chop until very fine or a smooth paste. Then add all of the ingredients into a saucepan, simmer for about 10 minutes and then remove the cardamom pods. Let the mix cool for a little while and then pour into an ice cube tray and freeze. Once frozen, remove from ice cube tray and blend in the food processor to make the ice cream texture. You may need to re-freeze this once blended, depending on the strength of your blender. Great served with the brownies or just some grated dairy-free chocolate on top.

Nutritional Breakdown

MACRO STATS	PER 100g	PER SERVING (62g)
CALORIES	*296*	*148*
CARBOHYDRATE	*21g*	*10.5g*
PROTEIN	*4.3g*	*2.15g*
FAT	*21g*	*10.5g*